Ezra Jagger's top five reasons to marry:

1. The promotion he's been dreaming about will be secured. (His boss has some concerns about sending a handsome bachelor to an island full of single and seeking women.)

2. His matchmaking relative, Miranda, will stop sending him on personal-ad dates. (He's not too good at making small talk with strange women. Except for one very attractive stranger, that is....)

3. Prospective bride Pawnee Walker won't take no for an answer. (And he's never been one to deny a beautiful woman *anything*.)

4. He's been wondering what waking up next to Pawnee each morning will be like. (And hoping he'll have the chance to find out soon after the wedding!)

5. He can't ignore the pounding of his heart every time his wife-to-be is near. (Not that love's got anything to do with this marriage....)

Alexandra Sellers wrote her first short story (about cats) at the age of ten, but, because her pencil couldn't keep up with her thoughts, asked her older sister to write it down for her. Unfortunately, rather than taking dictation, her sister recast the story in her own words. Alexandra's early compositions are thus lost to posterity. Alexandra didn't seriously sit down to write again for almost twenty years. NOT WITHOUT A WIFE! is her seventeenth novel.

NOT WITHOUT
A WIFE!

BY

ALEXANDRA SELLERS

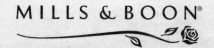

MILLS & BOON®

First published in Great Britain 1998
Harlequin Mills & Boon Limited,
Eton House, 18-24 Paradise Road, Richmond, Surrey, TW9 1SR

© Alexandra Sellers 1997

ISBN 0 263 81062 3

Set in Times Roman 10.5 on 12.25pt.
01-9808-47293 C1

Printed and bound in Norway
by AiT Trondheim AS, Trondheim

1

Are You A Canadian Citizen Going Out To A Posting Soon In Shamsirabia? I Would Like To Talk To You. *Urgent.* Please Call 555-1679. Anytime.

The ad, on a torn bit of newsprint, fell onto the table as he took his credit card out of his wallet. Ezra Jagger blinked at it for a moment, and then remembered: he'd seen it in the personal ads when Miranda was showing him the Companions Wanted column and, feeling a mild curiosity, had torn it out. Then he'd completely forgotten its existence.

He picked it up and fingered it absently before slipping it back into the wallet. Then, hesitating over his credit card, he fell to a contemplation of more immediate problems. Angela had gone to the ladies' room, and the waiter had brought him the bill without his asking for it. Should he pay it now, or would she want something more—another coffee, or a liqueur? If she'd sent him any signals, he sure hadn't picked them up. Was she enjoying his company, or was she bored?

He wasn't bored—he was too uncomfortable for

that. Angela was cute, Miranda had been right about
that, and he guessed she was brainy, too, but he'd
been too nervous even to eat properly, never mind
find out whether he liked her or not.

"Hi," she said, in her high, slightly breathy voice,
and he looked up to find her looking down at him
with a bright little smile. The smile made him anxious. Was she smiling like that because she liked him,
or because she thought he was a jerk? God, he hated
this. He hated dating even women he knew, let alone
complete strangers. Why had he let Miranda talk him
into this?

He half stood as Angela slipped into her chair opposite him. The waiter came back and hovered with
his hand near the little tray with the bill on it, waiting
for the credit card still in Ezra's hand to drop. Ezra
felt a buzz of irritation along his nerves. He glanced
up. "I'll let you know, okay?" he said softly.

The waiter disappeared as if he'd never been, and
Angela giggled. "You scared him to death," she observed, with some satisfaction.

He glanced at the waiter's retreating back.
"What?"

"Isn't that what you meant to do?"

All he'd wanted was a little peace to sort out what
he should be doing. It was a good, fairly expensive
restaurant, but half the tables were empty, and Ezra
didn't see why he should be railroaded into leaving
at the waiter's convenience. It wasn't even ten
o'clock.

His irritation made him forget his nerves. "I
wanted him to back off, that's all. He's brought the

damn bill, but would you like something more? Another coffee, a liqueur?''

Angela blinked. She knew why the waiter had brought the bill. She'd secretly asked him to, on the way to the bathroom. She didn't think she'd ever met a man who had less to say for himself than Ezra Jagger, and up to now the evening had been painful. She thought she'd save them both the embarrassment of spending any longer over it.

But in that second of irritation with the waiter, Ezra was suddenly someone else. Someone else rather masculine and attractive, as if some social layer had been stripped away, letting her see who he really was. He was a big man, good-looking in an un-Hollywood, rough kind of way, with thick dark brown hair and a full lower lip that she hadn't quite taken in before. Angela decided he might be worth a little more time and trouble.

So she sandbagged the poor waiter, who was in the background now just waiting to be summoned back to take the card with a discreetly righteous sniff. ''That would be nice,'' she smiled. ''A Cointreau, please?''

A raised finger brought the waiter, but his supercilious smile faded when Ezra said, ''A Cointreau and another black coffee.''

The bill disappeared discreetly from the table as the waiter threw a reproachful glance at Angela. Of course he'd violated the tenets of good waiting for her sake, and now he was probably going to lose his tip as a result. Angela flicked an apologetic eyebrow and began to think of ways she could slip him a fiver to make up for the probable loss.

"So tell me why you've got Miranda looking for a woman for you," Angela said, when the drinks had arrived.

Ezra laughed. It was an attractive laugh. Angela began to think Miranda might have been telling her the truth about Ezra—that he might be the "great catch" she'd said he was.

"If you could tell me how to stop her," he said.

Angela tilted her head. "Is she related to you? She explained, but I didn't take it in."

"She's my sister's future mother-in-law. She put her son and my sister together through some kind of personal ad and now she thinks she can match up the rest of the world, as far as I can make out. I came home for Christmas from Saudi and suddenly I was next on her list."

Angela laughed. "You didn't ask her to do it?"

"As I remember it, I asked her *not* to do it."

"But she thinks you need help finding a woman? I must say you don't look it." Not now.

"It's because I'm going out to Shamsirabia on my next assignment. Andy thinks I'd be happier if I took a wife with me."

"And what do you think?"

Ezra shrugged. "It's true you don't get much chance to meet women in Muslim countries." And he seemed to have drawn nothing but Muslim countries for the past five or six years. But he had no intention of marrying in haste in order to provide himself with the creature comforts, no matter how inhospitable the desert was.

"Do you like the match she made for your sister?"

"Ben's a guy I'll like as brother-in-law a helluva

lot more than Justin McCourt,'' he had to admit. ''My sister was engaged to him before Andy started working on it.''

''Your sister was engaged to *Justin McCourt?*'' Angela said breathlessly.

''Yeah, do you know him?''

She shook her head. ''He's a prof at the university. He's the man who made me wish I was majoring in English instead of Arabic.''

''Well, I'm glad Sam isn't marrying him. I never liked him.''

He'd heard all about the majoring in Arabic over dinner. It was one reason Miranda thought she'd found him the perfect match in Angela. ''She's really cute, Ezra, *and* she speaks good Arabic. She's very interested in Middle Eastern societies. Won't you find that useful in Shamsirabia and all those other Arab countries?''

He hadn't had the heart to tell Miranda that the sooner he saw the last of ''Shamsirabia and all those other Arab countries'' the happier he'd be. He was just waiting for the day he had enough seniority with Polygon Engineering to be offered a choice of assignments. What would Angela do with her Arabic in Alberta or Oregon? Or even Albania?

''Really?'' She fixed him with an enquiring eye over the lip of her liqueur glass, reminding him of his discomfort. Whatever he thought about Justin McCourt, he knew damned well that there wasn't a woman breathing who wouldn't prefer to be sitting here right now with handsome, debonair Justin McCourt rather than Ezra Jagger, though if he thought about it for a year he'd never be able to figure out what the draw was. "Why not?"

Ezra shrugged. "He's just not a man's man." He could see she wasn't happy with that. She wanted him to go on and do the details, but what was there to say? He didn't like the guy, he never had, though he'd tried his best for Sam's sake.

"Sometimes men who aren't men's men make the best husbands," Angela observed.

"She's ten times better off with Ben. A thousand."

"And so you're letting Miranda perform the same magic for you?"

"I don't know about Miranda's magic. As far as I can make out, that isn't the match Miranda planned on at all. She had another woman in mind for Ben. I'm not sure why she's so convinced she's got the matchmaker touch, but she is."

"Hmm," Angela grunted and sipped her liqueur. A silence fell between them again, and Ezra's heart began to register anxiety. He really would have to tell Miranda to quit this. He'd really have to put his foot down. The problem was, he liked Andy. He didn't want to hurt her feelings. But if the price was going to be a string of acutely uncomfortable evenings in the company of strangers from now till he left for Shamsirabia, maybe he'd just have to.

Somehow the conversation never got off the ground again, and there he was, dropping Angela off at her door by a few minutes past ten. She looked across at him in the faint streetlight as she unhooked her safety belt, but even if he'd wanted to, he didn't think he could have kissed her. He didn't know if he wanted to. She was cute, and her look even seemed to invite him, but Ezra just didn't know.

After a moment, she said, "Well, thanks very much. I enjoyed myself." And then she climbed out of the car and Ezra heaved a sigh as the tension left him.

"How did it go?" Sam called from the bedroom, in her seat in front of the computer. She had moved her computer desk in there when Ezra came to stay, because he was sleeping on her sofa.

"The same as the last one," Ezra said with a rueful grin. "Miranda's got good taste, I guess, but..." He shrugged and faded off. "How's the article?"

She was writing to a deadline of tomorrow morning.

"It's fine. I've broken the back of it, and now it's just getting it done. Another hour will do it." She punched *save*, pushed back the keyboard and got to her feet. "Would you like a coffee or something?"

"Have we got a beer?" He pulled off his tie and tossed it on the sofa as Sam moved to the kitchen. His jacket followed, and then Ezra flopped down, too. "I've had too much coffee."

She brought him the open bottle and a glass. Ezra ignored the glass and took a long, comforting pull of the beer.

"It makes you so uncomfortable, Ezra. Why don't you tell Andy?" Sam asked.

He shrugged. "Oh, I don't know. Maybe because...you know, I kind of wonder if Mom would have been like that. Egging me on to get married and give her grandchildren."

Sam nodded and stirred her coffee. "Yeah, I felt the same."

"All the arranging is kind of fun—watching her plot everything…it's only when I'm out there on my own with a strange woman that I realize what I've let myself get suckered into."

"It's all that stuff from Grandmother and Grandfather that did it, I guess."

Ezra looked up. "What stuff?"

"Oh, you know—they were always nagging you about the dangers of being alone with a member of the opposite sex. Probably—"

"Really?" he interrupted. "I don't remember that."

Sam looked surprised. "Gosh, I do. I didn't realize it then, but looking back I see that it started as soon as you hit puberty. They kept telling you you couldn't trust yourself with a girl now…don't you really remember?"

Ezra shrugged. "Vaguely, now you mention it. I don't suppose it had much effect."

"Well it sure had an effect on me. I kept wondering what kind of 'animal' you would turn into. They used to give you a terrible time before you went out on a date. It was very unpleasant stuff. I suppose they just didn't know how to cope with the problem of sex education."

Ezra shrugged. All he could remember was that he'd hated dating from day one. He finished his beer, then glanced at his watch. Ten-thirty. He suddenly found himself thinking about the ad in his wallet. If he called now he might get an answering machine message that would give him some clue about the advertiser. When Sam set down her cup and moved into her bedroom again, he reached for the phone.

"Hello?" It was a woman's voice, plain and firm with no breathy nonsense about it, any age between twenty and fifty. Ah well, so much for answering machines.

"You're running an ad in the *Globe and Mail*," said Ezra.

"Are you a journalist?" said the voice.

"Sorry, no. Is that what you want? I'm a construction engineer."

"Oh, that's great! And you're going out to..." she coughed. "When?"

"A couple of weeks," he answered evasively. "Mind telling me what this is about?"

"Not over the phone, though," she said firmly. "Where are you? Could you meet me?"

Ezra frowned and glanced at his watch. "Now?"

"If you're not out of town."

"I'm at College and Spadina."

"Hey, are you really? That's great! Do you know *Imam Bayaldi's* at the corner of Dean?"

"I'll find it."

"I'll be there inside of twenty minutes. Will you meet me?"

He felt so caught up in her excitement that he only said, "Okay."

"Let's not exchange names on the phone. I've got dark hair, I'll wear a red scarf." She put the phone down.

Sam smiled at him from her place in front of the computer as he appeared in the doorway. Of course his voice had carried. "Another blind date already?"

He pulled out his wallet, extracted the ad and handed it to her. Sam obligingly read it. Her eyebrows went up. "What do you suppose it's about?"

"Dunno. It caught my eye the other day when I was reading Miranda's hopefuls."

"Sounds as if they want you to carry something out there for them, or go and see someone, don't you think?"

"I guess I'll find out."

He didn't bother with his tie or his jacket this time, or his dress coat. Instead he pulled his bomber jacket out of the closet, wrapped a scarf around his neck and said goodbye.

"Don't get kidnapped by terrorists," Sam warned.

"Always a risk," Ezra agreed, and closed the door behind him. He supposed it was a risk, the way things were just now in Shamsirabia, but what would anybody want with a construction engineer?

It was snowing again outside, big thick feathery flakes, and he didn't bother with the company car he'd been loaned. The café was only about ten minutes away and he hadn't been home so long that he wasn't still enjoying the snow. You could get awfully homesick for winter in the desert sometimes. Ezra breathed the ice-cold air into his lungs and felt how fresh and clean it was.

Imam Bayaldi's was a place he'd previously avoided. He hadn't come all the way to Toronto to start hanging out at a Middle Eastern café. But it wasn't too bad, he reflected when he got inside. Small tables, good lighting. There were quite a few people sitting by themselves, deep in books, and he realized it was a place single people could come to just to be part of the bustle of humanity.

He sat down in a corner and was watching the door when a very slim, dark-haired woman with a red scarf came in and stood calmly looking around. Ezra raised a hand and she smiled and nodded as she headed for his table.

"This is really good of you," she said, unzipping her jacket and unwrapping her scarf as she stood. She was an ordinary looking woman, about twenty-three, he thought, with mid-brown eyes and dark brown hair that fell just short of her shoulders. She wore it tucked behind her ears in a no-nonsense fashion that insensibly relaxed him. Flakes of snow clustered over the top of her head like a hat, and as she sat she swiped one hand over her scalp and matter-of-factly shook it onto the floor.

"That's okay," said Ezra. He was half frowning, half smiling in puzzlement. Although she was pale enough to seem unhealthy, and hollow-eyed, under it she looked far too straight-up-and-down for all the skulduggery on the phone. She looked like someone who'd be happy milking cows. Well, maybe they recruited spies to look just like that. Who knew?

"My name's Pawnee," she said in a low voice, holding out a cool hand still slightly damp from the snow.

He took it. "Ezra."

"Do you mind if I ask you a couple of questions first, before telling you anything?"

Ezra paused. "I don't promise to answer them."

"No, okay. You're stationed in Shams?"

"Not yet. I came home for the holiday and they told me I was being reassigned there."

"What city are you going to?"

"The capital. Maqamallah."

She sighed and smiled. "That's great. That's just where I want to be. Look, would you—would you be willing to take me out there as your maid or something?"

"As my *maid?*"

She nodded urgently. "Do you have kids? Maybe I—"

He shook his head and she made a face. "Oh, too bad. I figure a mother's helper would be the easiest. Sort of what they expect, you know. What sort of job will you be doing out there?"

Ezra folded his arms and leaned on the table. "I think we've got to the point where you're going to have to tell me what this is about."

She sat still for a moment, eyeing him doubtfully, as though trying to guess what sort of man he was. Not in any romantic or sexual way, but in his character. It wasn't the way women usually looked at men, he thought, and it didn't make him at all uncomfortable.

"I don't know anything about you," she said at last. "Can I trust you? I mean, can I tell you something and you'll keep quiet about it if it turns out you can't help me?"

He looked back at her, trying to assess her in his turn. Her gaze seemed honest, if troubled. Hard to imagine her as a smuggler or drug runner, or even some kind of political weirdo.

"Is it illegal, immoral, or dishonest?" he asked.

She made another face. "No...not really."

Ezra sat back. "I don't think I can help you."

She put out an impulsive hand to restrain him. "No, wait! Please wait! You're my best chance so far. At least let me tell you about it!"

Maybe it was the complete lack of feminine wiles as she said it that got him. He always felt women were trying to manipulate him when they pouted, or flirted with their eyelashes or put on those pleading hangdog faces. It always made him feel at a disadvantage. But Pawnee just looked at him, kind of man-to-man.

"If it's anything like drugs you can't count on my silence," he warned.

"No, no!" Pawnee said impatiently. "It's nothing like that. Listen…" She glanced around the coffee shop, but they were speaking in lowered voices and there was some kind of Middle Eastern music playing, low but with the wailing tones that drown out the human voice. "Have you heard of Cree Walker?"

Of course he'd heard of Cree Walker. Every Canadian not in a vegetative state had heard of the woman who was being held hostage by rebels in Shamsirabia, but Ezra had a particular reason to remember the name. The unrest in Shamsirabia was what was causing the monarchy there to build a new mosque as a matter of urgency. It was also causing Polygon to take extra insurance on all the men heading out to the project. And a few other precautions.

"Yeah," was all he said.

"Cree's my sister," said Pawnee. "Nobody's lifting a finger to help. I've got to get out to Shams and bring her back."

2

He gawked at her, like a fish getting oxygen in a form it can't process. "Are you nuts?" he demanded, so loudly that two people glanced curiously up from their reading.

Ezra lowered his voice. "You're gonna go and— what? Tackle a bunch of rebels single-handedly like some damn movie hero and bring your sister out? You'll get yourself killed, that's all, and probably your sister, too."

She gazed steadily at him. "I'm not going to do anything in a hurry. What we mostly want is news. They don't tell us anything. My parents are sick with worry, and—"

"Oh, and it'll make them feel a hundred percent better to have two daughters in the same situation!" Ezra said sarcastically.

"Look," said Pawnee evenly. "Would you mind your own business? I don't need your big, strong masculine protection here, okay? Or your superior brain. I know what I'm doing and what I want to do. All I want to know from you is whether you'll help me."

It was direct without being mean, just a pure statement of facts. Ezra subsided. It wasn't like him to go all chauvinistic with a woman—usually just the reverse. He grinned. "Sorry. I'm a bit wound up about Shams. It's another damned desert kingdom, and one I could do without. We're getting so many rules in our Familiarization I feel as though I should be afraid to spit there, and here you are talking about single-handedly going after the bunch of lunatic revolutionaries that are causing it all."

"I thought Shamsirabia was pretty Western and liberal," Pawnee said.

"It was. But the monarchy know they're on shaky ground. They're catering to the rebels now. So basically it's another assignment where it's the death penalty for smuggling in a bottle of beer."

Pawnee got excited. "You see! That's what I've been saying all along! That they're not doing anything to find out where Cree is being held! They're just playing a waiting game. And I don't like people playing a waiting game with my sister!"

He looked at her. "It's beyond me what you think you can do about it. And anyway, why don't you just fly out there, if that's what you want? Why all the secrecy?"

"I made the stupid mistake of telling External Affairs that's what I was going to do. They told me very plainly that I shouldn't go, that it would 'upset the delicate balance' and annoy the government. All that kind of stuff. I think if I'm seen flouting their advice they'll do something tricky to prevent me."

"Like what? You're a citizen, aren't you? Ottawa haven't banned travel to Shamsirabia yet. We wouldn't be going if they had."

"Well, if they can't pull my passport, I wouldn't

put it past them to signal the Shamsirabian authorities who I was and get me refused a visa.''

''Ah—yeah, I guess it would be pretty easy to do.''

''So that's why I need you. If I'm going out as your maid or nanny or something, nobody'll notice me,'' Pawnee explained, with deceptive reasonableness.

''They won't notice a name like Pawnee Walker?'' Ezra asked dryly.

She shifted impatiently. ''My mother and her bright ideas!'' she muttered. ''It's all because she's so proud of having Indian blood! But, don't you see, they won't be looking for me to go out as a maid! Walker's a common enough name, anyway. And the Shamsirabians probably don't know I exist. I've been mostly dealing with Ottawa. I'm really not intending to get into trouble—I just want to see for myself what's going on out there.''

Ezra nodded understandingly. The case of Cree Walker had certainly caught the imagination of Canadians, his own included. She had been working as English tutor to a wealthy Shamsirabian diplomatic family and had gone there with them. The family had taken their responsibilities so lightly that they apparently hadn't even notified the authorities when Cree disappeared. It was only when the rebels announced that they were holding her that the family had admitted she'd been missing for three days. They said that they'd assumed she'd simply left their employ without telling them. She was, after all, a western woman and therefore not virtuous. She'd probably gone off with a man.

Canada had responded with terrible indignation.

Editors had blazed away with all guns at everybody involved. The Department of External Affairs, with oil not least among their concerns, had been somewhat less emphatic.

Ezra lifted his long, strong hands in a gesture of helplessness that did not suit them. "Yeah, I can understand that. I guess. But I'd be no help to you at all."

She fixed him with that man-to-man look again. "Why not?"

"Because not only do I not have kids, I have no wife. I wouldn't be able to take a woman to Shamsirabia as anything at all unless I were married. They'd assume you were there for immoral purposes, and I'd be declared persona non grata."

"Couldn't you try? I'm a pretty good manager, and not a bad cook, either. I mean, you know, I could fake it as cook-housekeeper," Pawnee said desperately.

He shook his head. "If I tried that on Polygon I wouldn't get past first base. *They'd* think it was for immoral purposes. Labour out there is so cheap I can hire a cook-housekeeper for six months on less than what it would take just to fly you there."

She subsided at last, accepting it. He felt like a monster, but he wasn't saying anything that wasn't the truth. Over the years, as they liked to point out regularly, Polygon had seen every trick in the book. It wasn't worth anyone's while trying anything that violated local laws.

"Look," he said. "I know it's hard, but look on the bright side. *Hezbuddin* so far aren't on record as having hurt any hostage, though they've had quite a few over the past couple of years. They generally get some compromise from the government and then release the hostage unharmed.''

''Cree's a woman,'' Pawnee said flatly. Her mouth was working and he guessed she wanted to cry. Ezra felt like even more of a heel. ''She's the first female hostage they've taken.''

''Yeah, I know,'' he said quietly, not looking at her.

She took a very obvious grip on herself and smiled. ''Well, thanks for listening, anyway. Gee, we haven't even had a coffee or anything! Can I get you something before you go out into the snow again?''

He glanced around. The place didn't seem to have any liquor licence. ''I've had too much coffee already,'' he said apologetically.

''Okay.'' She began to pull her jacket around her, and he was dimly aware of a reluctance to let her go like that. She must be desperately disappointed, however well she hid it, and he'd offered no help at all.

''Look,'' he said. ''If you want—I mean, I'll be there. I can keep my eyes open, look around…''

She smiled politely. ''That's very kind, but you wouldn't want to jeopardize…''

''No, I mean it. I can't do what you want, but I'd like to do something. What—''

Suddenly she was interested again. Her eyes glowed, and he thought how strange it was that a little thing like interest behind the eyes could turn a face from ordinary to almost beautiful. She leaned forward. ''Did you say this was a new project?''

''Yeah, that's right.''

"Is your company—would they be taking, say, secretaries out there?"

"The office staff has to be men."

"Oh." She was daunted again for a moment. Then, "But there must be some married couples going out with the project, aren't there? I mean, are married men allowed to take their wives?"

"Yeah, they are."

"Do you know anyone who's going out there with you?"

"I meet them all in the Familiarization training," Ezra said, knowing what was coming.

"Could you—is there anyone you know well enough to approach for me, explain what I want? I mean, if you talked to a wife, I know a woman would feel for me."

Ezra felt an irritated sense of injustice. "Damn it, *I* feel for you! I said so! It's just that what you ask is impossible."

"I'm sorry, I'm sorry, I didn't mean it the way it sounded." She put the pacifying hand on his arm again, and he got the feeling that she was used to calming people through touch. For the first time he wondered what she did for a living. Something she could drop at short notice, obviously. "But you did say that a family would be able to take someone, didn't you?"

He said, "Are you a nurse?"

"No, I thought of that, too. They do allow female medical personnel into Shamsirabia, but it would take ages just to get minimal qualifications."

"What are you?"

That level, assessing gaze found his. He noted with

approval how the square-set dark eyebrows gave her a look of direct honesty. "I'm a farmer," she said. "Or at least I would be, if we hadn't lost the farm. I was going to take over from my dad when I graduated from Agricultural College. Right now, I just do anything that earns money. It's not easy for a woman to get a farm job in this economic climate. Well, not to run a farm, anyway. I could be a housekeeper fast enough, but I'd hate that. I want to do farm management."

"Pretty tough work…"

"For a woman," she finished for him, without hostility. "Yeah, but maybe you haven't noticed I'm a pretty tough woman."

He grinned. "Well, fearless, I noticed that."

It suddenly occurred to him that they'd been talking for half an hour and he hadn't once felt uneasy in her presence. He hadn't got tongue-tied, either. He'd talked to her just the way he would to a man.

"Look, at least will you keep my number?" she said. "And call me if you think there's anyone who might be willing to help?"

He blew out a resigned breath. "Yeah, just so long as you understand—"

"I understand," she interrupted. "But you never know, do you? And would you—could I possibly have your number?"

He was almost certainly getting into something he'd regret, Ezra told himself. If he was her only lifeline she'd probably phone him six times a day to ask for news and drive him nuts. But somehow he found himself dictating Sam's phone number as she wrote in a neat little diary.

He pocketed the little torn-out page with her own name and number that she handed him even though he still had the ad, and then they were on their feet and pushing out into the still-falling snow.

"Thanks a lot, Ezra," she said. "Be talking to you."

He nodded. "Goodbye. Good luck. I'm sure your sister will be released unharmed."

"You bet," was all she said, and then he was alone in the whirling snow. He pulled his collar up and shivered. The temperature had dropped.

"How did it go last night?" Miranda demanded the next evening. "Did you like her?"

"I liked her all right, but there's nothing I can do for her," Ezra said. He was sitting in his usual seat at Miranda's left. The table was as full as ever on a Sunday night, with the whole family and then some in attendance, but there was a buzz of many conversations and Andy was talking for his ears alone.

"Nothing you can do for her?" Andy repeated in astonishment. "What do you mean? She didn't like you?"

He suddenly realized which *she* was under discussion. "Oh!" he said lamely. "Sorry, you mean Angela. She's all right, I guess, but we didn't hit it off."

Miranda let Angela go without a sigh. "Ah, well, it's early days yet," she assured him kindly. "I went through yesterday's and today's paper and found some very interesting people. The weekend papers carry more ads, you know."

"They do?"

"Oh, yes, it stands to reason, doesn't it? People

have time to browse on the weekend. Also, they're more likely to feel lonely and want to do something about it if it's Saturday night and they're alone. So that's when smart people advertise.''

He grinned at her. It really was impossible to resent Miranda. "How do you know all this?"

"Observation, that's all. I like to read the companions ads and fit different people together. Sometimes—don't tell any of this mob, they'd only laugh—sometimes I write to some of the box numbers and ask them if they've noticed a particular ad. I enclose the ad. I say it seems to me the person might suit them.''

"Does it ever work?" Ezra asked, bemused.

"Well, I don't know! I've never thought of giving my address and asking for a report. Maybe I should.''

"Maybe you shouldn't. What if it's a big mistake? They might blame you.''

"Oh, I don't think so, Ezra. I mean, look at Sam and Ben. They're perfect for each other, you told me that yourself.''

"Yeah, but—you wanted to set Ben up with Judith, didn't you?''

"Shh!" She glanced fearfully towards where Ben was sitting beside Sam.

Ezra laughed. "Andy, everybody knows. The whole story was explained to me with great gusto at this table.''

"Yes, but there's no point bringing it up all the time. Anyway, probably it was subconscious. Coincidence is a funny thing. I don't believe there's any such thing myself. I think probably my subconscious worked out how to get Sam. And you know she was engaged to that awful McCourt son. She'd never have answered a real companions ad, now, would she?''

She always lost him at moments like these. Sensing it, she switched tacks. ''So, who is the she you can't do anything for?''

''Sworn to secrecy, Miranda,'' said Ezra cruelly.

''Oh.'' Daunted, she took a sip of her wine. ''Well, then of course you can't—is it an old friend, or something?''

''No, someone I never met before.''

''Oh! Is it something to do with your work?''

He laughed. It was the laughter of pure enjoyment. He thought of all the years when no one had shown any real interest in his life, except for whether he was keeping up with his schoolwork and whether he'd jumped the girl he'd taken out. ''Are you keeping up with your schoolwork, Ezra?'' ''Yes, Grandmother.'' ''Good.'' ''I hope you behaved yourself tonight, Ezra.'' ''Yes, Grandfather.'' ''Good.'' Sam was right, though he'd only remembered when she reminded him. There had been a humiliating scene before and after every date in high school. No wonder he'd been terrified of dating. Still was.

''You might say that.''

''What did you do about that other ad, by the way?''

Damn. Ezra stirred uncomfortably. Maybe she was right. Maybe she had a subconscious laser beam. Something warned him not to tell her about Pawnee's problem. He had the feeling that if these two particular women ganged up on him he'd be no match for them. He'd end up doing something he didn't want.

Something stupid and chivalrous that would lose him his job, say. "What one was that?" he temporized.

"What was it—you remember, you noticed it in the paper when we were going over the ads. Some researcher or something to do with Shamsirabia."

Under the table, Ezra kicked Sam twice, with a pause between. It was an old, old signal—a request for some quick interference running. The situation now was very different from those disastrous meal scenes with their grandparents, but he was nearly as desperate.

"Oh, Andy!" Sam jumped and whirled in automatic response. "I meant to tell you! Ah..." He could see his sister was beating her brains for an idea. "...did you know Michael Welsh is having another show at the Johnson Gallery in two months?"

"Yes, why?"

"Oh, I just thought I'd tell you I've put in an idea with *Woman 2 Woman* for a layperson's art review. I've told them that for a kickoff feature I could maybe get a personal interview with him."

"Goodness, whatever possessed you to do that?"

"Well, I was kind of hoping you might...you know, ask him for me."

"Sam, I wouldn't dream of it. I treasure my relationship with Michael, and he hates any kind of personality publicity."

"Couldn't you just try this once?"

"Sam, he'll only tell me to tell you to write about his work, if you have the ability, or shut up if you don't. And that would mean I'd used up a favour, and I might need a favour from Michael one day."

Sam subsided with evident good grace. "Pity you

won't be here to come to the show with me, Ezra,''
she said next. ''Have you got your departure date
yet?''

''There's an awful lot of delay going on.'' Shielded
from Miranda's gaze by Ezra's shoulder, Sam crossed
her eyes dramatically at him. He knew what that
meant—she was sweating from having had to think
so fast. He wondered if she'd now have to make good
on the fib and suggest the art column to her editor.
His lips twitched, and he searched wildly for something to say so that he wouldn't laugh. He failed.
Suddenly he and Sam were snickering and giggling,
just as they used to. It was the one thing in which
they had defied their grandparents—their shared sense
of humour, which had always infuriated Grandmother
and Grandfather.

Not that Andy was in any way like them.

''Oh, Lord, the Jaggers are off again,'' said Jude
in mock exasperation as everybody stopped to look
at them.

''Yes, they're laughing at me this time, I don't
know why,'' Andy said without ill feeling.

''No, no, Andy!'' Sam protested, through her gig-
gles. ''Please don't take it personally, it's an old,
old...''

Ben caught Ezra's eye, his eyebrow raised, as if
he'd guessed it. Of course, Sam must have leapt out
of her conversation with him to come to Ezra's rescue.

''If you wouldn't shove people up against the wall,
Mom, they wouldn't call for reinforcements,'' he observed dryly.

''Oh, Ben, you always say things like that! I never

know what you mean. I haven't shoved Ezra up against any wall! I was just asking him about the women he's been meeting through the ads, that's all," Miranda protested.

Ben lifted his hands. "I rest my case."

"I don't see why that's your definition of getting someone up against a wall," Miranda protested indignantly. "Ezra's happy with what I'm doing. Aren't you, Ezra?" She turned suddenly. Her intonation was that of certainty, not of question, and he quailed.

"Well—" Ezra took a hasty sip of wine. He knew he couldn't begin to explain his mixed feelings on the subject. On the one hand he hated it, hated being forced to take out strange women and expose all his social inadequacies—to himself as well as to them. On the other, he enjoyed the relationship it gave him with Andy. He liked the feeling that she cared about his happiness. Seduced by that, he'd missed his chance to seriously tell her to butt out right at the beginning.

The horrified little frown forming behind her eyes was too much for him. "Yeah, sort of," he said hastily.

The whole table burst into laughter. "Now there's a real testimonial, Mom!" Luke said. "You'll go far on that!" Other comments also flew.

"I know exactly what Ezra means," Miranda said with dignity, over all the voices. "And we'll both thank you all to stay out of it. So, Ezra," she turned graciously back to him, "you don't want to say anything about the researcher you met. That's quite all right, I won't ask questions. Is she attractive?"

3

—◄—

"Of course, women's rights are being eroded in Shams, just like everywhere else in the Islamic world," Althea said in matter-of-fact dismissal. "The root of the problem is that the Mullahs don't want to face the necessity for a new interpretation of Shari'a. It's a kind of backlash against necessity."

Ezra wasn't sure exactly when his eyes had begun to glaze over. But looking on the bright side, at least it was easy to keep up his end of the conversation: listening.

Althea paused, but only to light another cigarette. She set down her smart gold lighter with a little clink and drew once to be sure the cigarette was working properly, then blew out the smoke. "A new interpretation of Shari'a based on what Mohammed actually said about women would throw all the traditional Islamic treatment of women out the window. Did you know that?"

"Ah, no, I don't think I did," Ezra responded brightly.

"No one knows it, but it's true. It's all there in the Koran. The thing is, for my research I've been planning to go out to someplace like Shams, where the

modern secular-based rights of women are being
eroded as a sop to Islamic militants who are threat-
ening the power structure. I want to watch the whole
process. Shams is ideal, really, because although the
process is already in train it's still very early on. I
mean, women aren't yet forced to wear the veil, are
they?''

The sudden question threw him. ''Oh—ah, I don't
know.''

The blue eyes assessed him in astonishment. ''You
don't know?'' was all she said, but he could see what
she thought of such ignorance.

Ezra started to sweat. Suddenly listening wasn't
good enough. ''The thing is—I mean, I haven't been
there yet.''

She nodded, blowing out smoke, not looking at
him. Probably to save him from the contempt that he
would have seen in her eyes, Ezra told himself.

''Yes, I see. I'm sorry, I thought you said you were
on an orientation or familiarization course or something. Has that not started yet?''

It was two hours before he could get away. He
returned to Sam's place and staggered out of the elevator about as limp as he ever wanted to be. The
place was dark, and when he opened the door the
alarm beeper signalled him to punch in the code. Sam
must be at Ben's.

Ezra felt up and down the wall for the hall light
switch. Usually Sam left it on when she went out, and
he realized suddenly that he had no idea where the
damn switch was. Somewhere in the darkness the
beeper threatened him with reprisal if he didn't cue
in the number *now*.

"Dammit, dammit, dammit!" Ezra shouted, groping ever more wildly for the switch, which was
clearly evading his hand for sinister reasons of its
own. The alarm changed tone, setting up a high
whine, which he knew gave him thirty seconds to
punch in the number or else. There was a subtle glow
coming from the pad: he'd probably be able to see
the numbers in the darkness. Leaving the door to the
communal hall wide to get the benefit of what light
there was, Ezra launched himself at the pad.

He stepped straight onto the phone, which had
placed itself right in the middle of the hall floor.
While he fought for balance, the phone cord wrapped
itself around his ankle and brought him down with a
crash.

The hall light went on. "Ezra? Can I help?"

He rolled and looked up. Marie, Sam's neighbour,
stepped lightly over his legs and keyed in the number.
The whine stopped.

"Please hang up. Please hang up," said a voice,
and then a different whine started from the receiver.
Marie bent down and put it back on the hook.

"Hi," she smiled wanly, and remained squatting,
at eye level with him in his position on the floor. "I
heard you shouting and figured you must be having
trouble with the alarm. Did you forget the number
again?"

"No, I couldn't find it in the dark," he muttered,
feeling like a jerk.

"Sam must have gone out this afternoon before it
got dark," Marie explained, unwinding the phone
cord from his left ankle. She stood up and put out a
hand to help him up. Lying there, Ezra raised his

eyebrows at her. She looked as though she weighed ninety-seven pounds carrying a poodle. How much of his weight did she imagine she could take? But for politeness' sake he wrapped his hand around hers as he got to his feet. Boy, did he ever feel like a dumb giant.

"Good night, Ezra," Marie said calmly. "I was just on my way to bed. I've got an early shoot tomorrow."

"Sorry to have disturbed you. Thanks for the rescue," he said.

"That's all right," she said.

As he closed the door, the phone rang at his feet.

"Is Sam—Ezra, is that you?" demanded an astonished Miranda.

"Yeah, it is, Andy. Sam's not home, I'm afraid."

"But Ezra, what are you doing there? You were supposed to meet that nice girl Althea tonight."

Did he need this right now? Did he, hell. He glanced guiltily at his watch. Ten to ten. About par for the course. "Yeah. Well, I did."

Miranda got the message instantly. "Oh, dear! And I thought she was so nice and intelligent."

"Very brainy," Ezra agreed.

"And she knows so much about Shamsirabia. Didn't she tell you?"

"All night," he couldn't help saying dryly.

Miranda giggled, and he knew she was going to let him off the hook. That was the good thing about Miranda—she never argued against the inevitable. "Yes, I did wonder if she was a little too—oh well, never mind! Plenty of fish in the sea, as my mother used to say, and I've got a really lovely girl lined up for

Thursday. Will you ask Sam to phone me tomorrow? It's not important, it's just a question about the wedding invitations. My friend Harold is printing them, you know.''

''I'll tell her.''

He'd been wearing his suit all day, and couldn't wait to get out of it. But he was only half-undressed when the phone rang again. ''*Now* what?'' he demanded aloud, right at the end of his rope. He scooped it up. ''Yeah,'' he said shortly.

''Ezra? Is that Ezra Jagger?'' said a female voice. He knew he'd heard the voice before. It must be one of Miranda's hopefuls. He closed his eyes. He just couldn't take any more hassle tonight.

''No,'' he lied feebly. ''He's not here.''

''Wow, you sound just like him. I'm sorry to ring so late. Will you tell him that Pawnee Walker called? It's urg—''

''Oh, Pawnee!'' Ezra burst out with relief before he could stop himself.

''Ezra? It's you? Oh, that's great!'' her voice sang. ''I've been phoning all night, no answer, and then the line was busy. I nearly went crazy. Look, Ezra, are you busy right now? Could you possibly meet me to talk?''

She made no reference to the fact that he'd lied about who he was. If she had, even a joking one, he'd have been embarrassed. He felt the relief of talking to a woman who didn't use every opportunity to make him feel guilty.

Maybe it was that that prompted him to consult his watch and say calmly, ''Sure. Same place? Fifteen

minutes?'' even though two minutes ago he'd been
positive he couldn't take any more tonight.

"Great," she said. "This time at least I'll buy you
a coffee."

It had stopped snowing. The night was clear, the
stars sparkling as if someone had just taken soap and
a brush to them, the wind smelling fresh because so
few cars were on the road. Ezra enjoyed the tramp
through the ankle-deep powder down Brunswick and
along College to the little café.

Her cheeks were pink with cold, and she was still
rubbing her hands when he entered, so she could only
have beaten him by seconds. She grinned and lifted
her arm as he closed the door behind him, though he
could hardly have missed her in the tiny space. There
was only one other patron.

"I ordered you a coffee, is that all right?" she demanded as he stripped off his bomber jacket and sat
down. "And a little snack. I felt guilty last time, we
sat here for ages and you didn't eat or drink a thing."

"It's okay," he said. "A passing guy gave me a
buck, so I didn't starve."

He didn't often joke with women, mostly they took
him seriously and he hated having to explain. Pawnee
laughed as if she really enjoyed the joke, which must
be a first. "Sorry, did I sound like your mother?" She
shook her head. "But I really should have—"

She broke off as two cups of steaming coffee and
a few little plates of Middle Eastern snacks and some
pita bread were slid onto the table. "Thanks," she
said, flashing a smile upwards at the chef-cum-waiter.
In busier hours, Ezra knew, you picked up your order

at the counter, but the snow meant there were few customers tonight.

"Do you know yet when you're leaving for Shamsirabia?" Pawnee asked, when the waiter had gone. She tore off a piece of pita bread and dug into the hoummos, and didn't look at him again until the tidbit was safely inside her mouth. Althea had gazed at him all through dinner, making him feel like a pinned insect. He could never relax when a woman was staring at him big-eyed.

He shook his head and had a go at the *baba ghanoush* himself. He actually liked Middle Eastern food; food wasn't one of the reasons on his list for not looking forward to the desert again. In fact, it really bothered him that the company cafeteria usually only served Canadian food, wherever the project was. As far as Ezra was concerned, food was usually the best thing about a foreign country.

"It was supposed to be next week, but it's been put off three days. No one's saying why."

"Oh, great! That'll give us time," said Pawnee.

Seeing the garden gate open, of course Ezra walked right in. "Time for what?" he demanded curiously, meanwhile fishing after an errant black olive that was eluding his pita.

"Time to get married without it looking too phoney."

Ezra's body just quit on him. He could feel himself turning into a statue right there, with his fingers in the *baba ghanoush* and all. Suddenly he realized his body was way too big for these little spindly tables and chairs.

Carefully he let go of the piece of pita, leaving it

there in the dish. Carefully he wiped his fingers on his napkin. Then he paused for another few seconds, still not looking at her.

"Oh, damn!" she said ruefully. "I knew I'd say it all wrong!"

He looked at her. "I don't think there would have been a right way," he pointed out carefully. "*Married* is one of those words it's hard to just throw at a complete stranger like that. I mean, I think you did it as well as anyone could," he assured her, when she tried to interrupt, "but I kinda wasn't expecting it. You'll have to tell me what I missed back there."

She laughed helplessly and dropped her forehead into her hand. "Damn, damn! No, you haven't missed anything, of course you haven't, it's just that I got myself all geared up to say it and then couldn't wait. Of course you think I'm crazy now! But I swear I'm not! It's just—the idea just came to me, like a lightning bolt, and it's so perfect, but I knew I had to ask you before I lost my nerve. I was phoning you all night, praying you'd come in before I weakened or it was too late to call. And you did."

She smiled. Just for one moment there Ezra had got the idea that Pawnee Walker had fallen in love with him at first sight. Just for a second. He'd realized even before she spoke again that it couldn't be that, but while he did think it, he'd had the strangest sensation in his gut.... He rubbed his nose uncomfortably and took a delaying sip of coffee.

"Look," she said reasonably. "Let me just explain, okay? I swear it's a good idea, I just put it to you too fast. And you'll—" She blew out an exasperated breath. "Can I just explain? Will you listen?"

"Sure," said Ezra. Women usually did like him at first sight; he was big and strong and good-looking in a football player kind of way. It was later they went off him. When he proved he couldn't flirt or flatter or do any of those social things women liked from men. If Pawnee *had* thought she'd fallen in love with him at first sight, he supposed honesty would have compelled him to explain that it wouldn't last.

He watched her across the table as she hunted for words. She was all right looking, he liked what he saw, and he guessed she had her share of dates, but probably she didn't have men beating down the door. Her dark hair was straggling a bit around her ears, and her face was too pale. She was probably way too thin; he noticed she'd only had the one mouthful of food, but she didn't look interested in any more. She had big dark eyes, but they had dark shadows around them, and all her fingernails were bitten right back. She was nibbling on one now, and frowning thoughtfully.

Maybe she wasn't that physically exciting as a woman, but from the start he'd kind of liked her as a *person*. If she *had* told him she loved him, who knew what he'd have said? Must be kind of nice to have someone in love with you, even if you only liked them.

These thoughts were compressed into the few seconds it took Pawnee to gather her own thoughts. Now she smoothed the finger she'd been nibbling and said, "Look, it's very simple. If you got married, naturally you'd want to take your wife with you to Shamsirabia, wouldn't you? I mean, it wouldn't raise any eyebrows at all."

That much was true. Guys were always speeding up their marriages in order to be able to take their girlfriends with them to a job. You didn't get married quarters unless you were married.

"I'm with you so far."

"Well—don't you see that's the way? If I keep asking people to take me with them sooner or later someone's going to tell the papers or even Ottawa, right? I suddenly realized I just can't take any more people into my confidence."

"How many people have you told so far?" Ezra asked.

She hung her head. "Just you. No one else has called. Well, there was one guy—some kind of desalination engineer, or something. There was just something about him that…I don't know. I wouldn't have gone to the end of the road with him, not without my keys in my hand. So I didn't tell him anything. But I knew I could trust you right away," she said, the dark, anxious eyes fixing him. She didn't mention that it was the contrast between the two men that had suddenly made Ezra stand out in sharp relief, had made her aware of the interesting fact that she had had no doubts about confiding in Ezra, no fear that he would take advantage of her position when they were in Shams. He was a good-looking guy, with thick dark hair like her dad's, but it wasn't that. He was a lot bigger than her, but she'd trusted him instinctively. "It was after meeting him that I realized what a risk it all is."

"I already told you what a risk it is."

"And I knew it had to be you or no one," she went on, as if he hadn't spoken. "And you said yourself there's only one way you can take a woman to Shamsirabia. Please, Ezra, would you marry me and take me out there as your wife? I've got to find Cree. Please.''

"And what'll you do once you find her?" he asked flatly.

"Bring her home." She sighed as she said it, as though that was all she was living for.

He sat there for a minute. "Do you think there's a gap in your plans?" he demanded, almost angry.

"What?" She looked at him with those haunted, hollow eyes, and he realized that she was definitely looking worse than the first time he'd seen her. She must be literally worrying herself sick. He pushed one of the little plates of food towards her.

"You ought to eat something," he offered awkwardly.

She didn't even glance at it. "Never mind that. What have I missed?"

"You go and find your sister and bring her home, and there you are in all the papers as the heroine, and I'm facing my boss and explaining how I cheated the company and the Shams immigration for you. Just how pissed off do you figure they'll be?"

"We can cover it up. I'll stay out of the limelight when we get back. You—"

"And then I'm a guy can't keep. his brand-new wife happy."

"Oh." She subsided completely, as though she'd been kept alive on excitement alone, and now that it was gone there was nothing to support her body. "Oh, God, you're right! I never thought of that." She looked at him. "I'm sorry, you must think I'm totally selfish, and I guess I am. But if you could see how this is killing my parents. Losing the farm was bad, but they managed that.'' She shook her head hopelessly. ''I don't think they'll survive this, not if it goes on for long. Sometimes these things take months, don't they? And I keep thinking of Cree, and what she might be going through...''

Ezra shifted uncomfortably on the tiny chair. ''Look, I told you before, I'll do something for you when I'm there. Whatever I can.''

''How long will you be out there, Ezra? Are you there right till the end of the project?''

''Once the interior guys take over, I'll be given a new assignment. I'm not project boss yet, the project boss is the one who stays till the last carpet is laid.''

''How long will that be?''

''If the locals know their stuff,'' he shrugged, ''four to six months, I guess.''

''I promise to stay till you leave Shamsirabia, whatever happens with my sister. That won't be so bad, will it? We can pretend to split up when we get back, and then to the men on your new assignment it would be just old history. Wouldn't it? Please marry me, Ezra.''

He staggered back to Sam's place feeling as though he'd been worked over with a baseball bat.

''Hi!'' Sam called from the bathroom. She was in pyjamas, brushing her teeth, her hair all bunched up on top of her head with an elastic. Her face was bright and fresh, she looked all shiny with happiness. She must have just said good-night to Ben. The contrast with Pawnee's unhappy, drawn face, still sharp in his memory, was almost painful. "It's after midnight. You must have had a good time," she observed with a smile, coming out into the hall and flicking off the light.

"Not exactly," Ezra said. He was glad she was home. He got lonely when he was off on a job; he was always glad to come home and feel part of a family for a while. For a moment he thought of telling her about Pawnee; he'd have liked to hear what his sister thought about it. But maybe he shouldn't. It wasn't really his story to tell.

Especially since he'd refused to do what Pawnee wanted. It hadn't been easy, but he was so sure he was right. She was asking for more trouble than she'd be able to handle, wanting to go to Shams and start messing around with terrorists. In the end she'd just sat there saying, *please, please.* He felt like a punching bag.

"Did you hear the news tonight?" Sam asked, coming in from the kitchen. She put down a loaded coffee tray and settled down on the sofa opposite him for a long winter's chat. "This is brewed decaf, by the way," she said in an aside as she poured.

"No, I've been out," said Ezra, accepting the cup and stirring sugar into it.

"I guess you'll hear it tomorrow. There's more trouble in Shamsirabia. They're saying that Canadian hostage is very sick or something. If the king won't give in to the rebels' demands, they'll let her die. Not their fault. God's will, you know," she said in dry outrage.

Sam finished pouring her own coffee, sipped it and looked up. "It's starting to look ugly, Ezra," she said worriedly. "I don't see how that situation can last. Do you have to go?"

He was staring into space, imagining Pawnee's reaction when she got home and heard that. For sure she'd hear it tonight from someone, no matter how late it was. He felt a little sick. It was ridiculous, her plan, but he supposed doing something was better than doing nothing.

When the silence had gone on a little too long, he shook himself into the here and now. "Yeah, I have to go," he told Sam, with a little shrug. "If they send the team, I have to go, or quit. Don't worry. Polygon has never yet had a serious problem. If there's too much trouble probably the project will be cancelled anyway."

She was still frowning. "Ben says it stinks, and you know he's got a lot of experience of that kind of situation. Ben says the monarchy is going to fall, and then there'll be civil war. Will you be able to get out of the country if that happens?"

Ezra made a face. "It's not as though we're in the hinterland, Sam. We'll be right there in the capital, which has a good, modern airport. If we move fast we can be out before they've finished storming the palace. Damn, I wonder how bad Cree is, though."

She looked at him, perplexed.

"Ahhh—you know, Cree Walker, the hostage."

"Golly, do you *know* her, Ez? I never knew that. I'm sure you never said."

"No, not her. I—um, know her sister a little."

"Oh, right. The one who's been agitating for Ottawa to do something. Must be hell, having a sister taken hostage. There's not really anything she can do, is there? How's she taking it?"

"Pretty hard." He thought about the dark-ringed eyes, the chewed fingernails. "It's really killing her, I think. She's got this idea she'd—" Well, here he was telling Sam about it after all. He broke off. "Sam, I don't have to ask you, do I? I mean, it would make a great story for some tabloid journalist."

She smiled gently, her head tilted to one side. "No, you don't have to ask me, Ez."

He heaved a sigh. "Pawnee wants to go out there and try to track those guys down. Bring her sister back, like Girl Rambo or something. I think she's crazy."

"I'm sure she is. If it were you, I'd be climbing the walls."

"Yeah, but would you go out there and start messing around?"

"How can I know what I'd do? I'd sure want to, if I thought there was something I could do. What kind of plan does she have once she gets there?"

Had he asked her that? It occurred to him now for the first time that Sam was right and that Pawnee must have some concrete plan of action, based on something she knew, that she hadn't told him about. "I don't know. All I know is her plan for getting there. She wants me to marry her and take her on the project."

Sam sloshed coffee on her pyjama leg. *"What?"*

He nodded.

"Boy, Ezra, that's a—are you going to do it?"

"No. I said no. It's—if she got into trouble, got kidnapped herself, Sam…"

The green eyes were dark with fellow feeling.
"Yeah, I'm sure you're right."

"Am I, Sam? Do you *really* think so?"

She paused. "I don't know, Ezra. Why are you
asking this?"

"Because I feel like a real heel. I'm sure I'm right,
but why do I feel so lousy, saying no? She might get
killed out there if I took her."

Sam looked at him. "Are you in love with her, is
that why you don't want her to get hurt?"

He blinked. "No, of course not! You don't have to
be in love with someone to want to stop them killing
themselves, do you?"

"Well, maybe not. But you said it's killing her
anyway. Why should she sit at home playing safe
when her sister might be dying?"

"So you think I should do it?" Ezra asked in surprise.

"I didn't say that. All I'm saying is, maybe *her*
judgement of what she should do is sounder than
yours. If you're not in love, why should you stop her
risking her life for what she believes in?"

"Good question." He hadn't seen it that way before, though he was pretty sure Pawnee had tried to
put that point of view to him. He guessed he hadn't
really listened to her because he thought he was right.
Now he heaved in air and blew it out through his lips.
"I don't know, Sam, it sure looks complicated to
me."

She said, a little alarmed, "I'm not saying you
should do it, Ez, just trying to show you she may have
a legitimate point of view. Maybe she's tough, maybe
she's not worried about physical danger the way you

think she should be. And maybe she'll get through whatever's coming a whole lot better if she's tried her best. That's all.''

"Hi," whispered the soft, throaty voice from the speakerphone. *"My name's Doro. They tell me I've got four minutes, and I don't want to waste any of it. So here it is. I'm slim, except where it counts, I'm blond with a little help from a bottle, I've got blue eyes that don't need any help at all, I'm five feet five inches tall, and men say I'm cute and funny and my teeth aren't teeth but pearls.''*

"That's a quote from a song, if you don't recognize it," Andy interjected quickly. "She's got quite a sense of humour, really."

Ezra glanced at her, saying nothing. He didn't like the voice at all, it was breathy and sounded false, conjuring up the image of a frothy, giggly blonde without common sense, just the kind of woman who made him most nervous. Pawnee's voice wasn't anything like that, for example. Before he'd even seen her he'd known she was a practical, no-nonsense kind of woman. Not that succeeding events had proven him entirely right, he reminded himself. Getting into a fake marriage was hardly an idea you'd call level-headed.

"Now, what kind of man do I want? Well, that's not so easy. I like big men, but I'm not going to say no just because someone's not a six-footer. I like—''

Ezra reached out and pushed the button to cut the connection. Miranda looked at him enquiringly. "No?" she said, disappointed. "It does get better as she goes along."

"It's all right right now, but I just don't—sorry, Miranda." He breathed and shook his head. "I guess I'm just not in the mood for this at the moment."

"Oh, Ezra, I did want to find you someone before you left."

"Andy, I'm not going to find a wife in under two weeks."

"No, I know you're not." She sighed. "I know there's not enough time now. But I thought, even if you had somebody to write to, someone to come home to, it would make it that much easier when you did. I mean, people do fall in love by letter, you know."

"I'm not much good at letter-writing. Ask Sam how many she gets. Maybe we should leave this till I'm home next time."

"Next time is the wedding. I won't have time to think."

"No, I mean, the next time I'm here for a break. For the wedding I won't get more than two days or so." Valentine's Day. *His* sister would be getting married to a guy she loved and who was crazy about her. He wondered what Cree Walker would be doing. How Pawnee's voice would sound then, if he called. Not very friendly, probably.

"Right," Miranda said. "You're right, I'm pushing this too hard, and I should just leave you alone. You haven't got much time and you don't want to spend every evening with a stranger, you want to see your sister."

"It's not that I mind," Ezra assured her, generous in victory. "But maybe one a week would be easier to handle."

She patted his knee. "Okay, Ezra, no more. Not unless I positively *trip* over Miss Right."

She couldn't understand why he was laughing so hard.

"I guess you've heard the news."

His heart started thumping as soon as he heard her voice. "Yeah. Yeah, I did."

"My grandmother's diabetic. My parents are afraid that Cree has developed diabetes because of the stress and—you know, the bad diet, bad water, everything. And that because it hasn't been diagnosed no one will have any idea what's wrong. They're convinced she's going to die."

He didn't answer. Silence fell, not even a crackle on the line. "Pawnee," he said at last.

"Ezra, I will do anything you say. I'll stay as long as you want, I'll pretend you're the one breaking it off and that it's killing me to leave you. I'm a good cook, I'm a good manager. Lots of things. You won't be sorry."

For some reason that made him mad. "What exactly are you offering?" he demanded furiously.

He heard the intake of her breath. Then, "What exactly do you want?"

"What I do not want is you selling yourself like some cheap—"

"I don't call it cheap," she interrupted, her voice soft but matter-of-fact. "My sister's life is worth a lot to me. Everything."

"Well, I don't need to be offered duty sex as an inducement to do something I have no intentions of doing anyway, and if I won't do it just to help you out, I'm sure not going to do it for sex!''

"I didn't offer sex, Ezra," she pointed out. "You're the one who brought it up."

"Or a cook, either!" he shouted. "What the hell do you think I am?"

"The only man in the world who can help me, at this point. That means you can name your own price, doesn't it?"

"Damn it to *hell!*" He'd never been so mad in his life. "I told you, I don't *have* a price! I told you I'm not going to do it! Will you stop talking to me as if I'm some bloated capitalist? I've said *no!*"

"Yeah, I know you have," she submitted abruptly. He could hear that she was utterly dispirited.

He was more angry with himself, now, than with her. Sex. What had made him bring that up? She must think... "You can't do any good anyway! Those guys are out in the wilds somewhere with her! How are you going to track them down from the middle of Maqamallah?" he demanded hotly. He thought of Sam saying, *Maybe she'll get through whatever's coming a whole lot better if she's tried her best.* "You haven't got any plans, any clues!"

"No," she said, after a moment. But he had heard the hesitation and suddenly his suspicions came to a head: There was something she wasn't telling him. She had some kind of plan in mind. Which made it even more dangerous, even more stupid for him to even consider the idea. He was looking at a whole passel of trouble if he even let her think he was weakening, and he ought to hang up right now, no apologies, and refuse to speak to her again. If he talked to her for too long he was in danger of starting to think it might be a reasonable thing to do, and if he gave in he'd be so many kinds of fool he couldn't count them. For sure, for sure, Pawnee with a plan was a lot more of a risky proposition than Pawnee without one. He'd just tell her no for the last time, hang up and let Sam's answerphone take care of things from now on.

Ezra cleared his throat. "Pawnee," he began firmly.

"Yeah, Ezra," she said tonelessly, as if she knew what was coming now, but knew she had used up her last ounce of ingenuity and had to give in to the inevitable.

"Pawnee...ah hell! Pawnee, will you marry me?"

4

The bride wore white. Miranda could understand the need for speed, but over her dead body were they going to get married at City Hall, like some marriage of convenience to an illegal immigrant.

No one except Sam and Ben knew that it *was* a marriage of convenience. The fewer people in on the secret the better. That was fine, Ezra reflected, but somehow it made Miranda's arguments impossible to withstand.

So they were married in the Harris living room one bright Sunday morning, two days before their departure for Shamsirabia. Pawnee looked drawn but happy in a creamy white wool suit that Sam had borrowed for her from a friend, a smart little matching hat that Miranda had found downtown yesterday just by chance—after four hours of hunting, in an expensive little boutique, but of course she told no one that—beige heels, and a bouquet of red and pink poinsettias.

Ezra didn't look happy. He looked worried and preoccupied, and when Miranda saw the grateful way Pawnee looked at him, as if the giant beside her were her saviour, she bit her lip. She supposed in most marriages one loved more than the other, but she'd always felt that that one should be the man. Women learned to love, and to trust, over time. She wasn't sure about men.

The whole family was there, of course. Pawnee's parents had only arrived at the last minute. They'd meant to come and stay the night, but the weather in Peterborough had been very bad Saturday, and the snowploughs hadn't got through till late evening. Thank God they'd made it this morning. Jack Walker was giving his daughter away, as surprised as any of them by the speed of the thing. So everything was going fine, Miranda told herself. She just wished Ezra looked happier.

It was time for the ring. Ben was best man, and Sam was the bridesmaid, in her lovely red dress that perfectly complemented the bride's bouquet. Ben didn't wear a suit often, but he was wearing one to-day, and as he reached into his pocket for the little gold band, Miranda saw him glance across at Sam with a look in his eyes that said he wished he hadn't promised to wait for a big wedding, and Miranda's throat tightened.

He placed the ring on the minister's open Bible. Ezra picked it up and Pawnee put her hand in his and smiled nervously up at him, as if wondering whether he might change his mind, and pleading with him not to.

Ezra slipped the ring on Pawnee's slender finger and held it there, glancing up into her face.

"With this ring I thee wed," said the minister, and Ezra repeated, "With this ring I thee wed."

He frowned, and blinked, a bit like a man who is waking up unexpectedly. The muscles of his hand tightened involuntarily on the ring...and then the look Miranda had been waiting to see came into his eyes. The look that said he suddenly understood why marriage was not to be entered into inadvisedly or lightly...the look that said he was looking at his *wife*.

Miranda sniffed as the tears came to her eyes.

The minister wouldn't stay, but it was a very large, cheerful group and they didn't miss him. First on the agenda was a champagne toast, and after that came the gifts. Pawnee was horrified. She hadn't expected any of this; you could tell by her face she felt that strangers shouldn't be buying her things.

"Oh—I wish you hadn't gone to so much trouble!" she exclaimed, when the little pile of presents was revealed.

"Now, never mind!" Miranda said, smiling. "We don't know each other very well, but you're family now, and you may as well get used to it. Anyway, they're all simple gifts. Nothing expensive."

Pawnee glanced at Ezra, but he only looked back impassively. How she wished they'd gone to City Hall! All this loving welcome made her feel just that much more of a fraud. But there was nothing to do now except open the gifts and play the happy bride.

Well, she was happy, if not for the reasons everybody thought. She was happy, and scared to death, so she guessed she wasn't so far off the emotional state of a real bride.

Mindful of the fact that the married couple would be flying off to Shamsirabia shortly, everybody had given simple gifts that could be packed easily. A calendar with the dates in both the Islamic and the Western year. A travel size Trivial Pursuit, and one of backgammon. Foldable sun hats. Pawnee opened them all, with Ezra beside her on the sofa and everyone else sitting around them, and smiled and thanked the givers. Luke and Carol's gift was last in the heap, even thinner and lighter than the others. Pawnee, wrestling with the tape, suddenly felt her hands shoot apart, tearing the paper and causing the contents to fly out. Ezra automatically caught it, and then there was a burst of applause as he involuntarily held it up.

A delicate thing of lace and silk, in creamy white, the kind of thing a bride would wear on her wedding night. It wasn't vulgar or crude, it was softly, warmly sexy, but Pawnee dropped her eyes and Ezra blushed bright red, and like a clap of thunder the whole room understood that these two had never yet made love together.

A kind of astonished, charmed silence fell over them all as Pawnee hastily snatched the gift from Ezra's very big, very masculine hand and tucked it back into the tissue. And then, because they were boisterous and earthy but not insensitive, the Harrises all started at once to talk about something else.

Late in the afternoon, Ben and Sam drove them down to Sam's place. Pawnee had given up her rented room yesterday and brought her bags over to Sam's, where she and Sam spent the night. Ezra had stayed with Ben.

Her parents were following them down, and would take a lot of her things back to Peterborough with them. Of course she hadn't told her parents the truth, any more than anyone else. If they knew what she was doing, and what she planned to do, they'd die rather than let her go. Her mother was suspicious, but Pawnee had been determined not to confirm those suspicions. They had enough to think about. And whatever the outcome of her plans, it would be far better for her parents' peace of mind if they'd had no share in them.

"We met because I was talking to anyone who knew anything about Shamsirabia," she'd admitted over the phone. "It's just one of those things. We fell in love."

"You don't sound as though you fell in love. You sound as though you've got something up your sleeve," her mother had observed trenchantly. "But I'm not going to tell your father. He already worries enough. All right, we'll be there, Pawnee. But I don't like it."

Now, as her father, Ezra, Ben and Sam carried down her boxes and cases to the car, she was left alone with her mother.

"Goodbye, Mom, I'll write," Pawnee said, as they embraced. Then they looked into each other's eyes. Pawnee wondered if this was the last time she would see her mother, and her throat tightened with tears. A calm, solid, practical kind of woman, her mother. The old-fashioned kind of farmer's wife. She didn't talk about feelings much, but there'd always been a sense of real security in her kitchen. She had absorbed the loss of the farm like a stone pillar, by a blow from a hammer, driven one inch further into the ground. The news about Cree had been different, though. That was the first time in her life Pawnee had seen her mother shaken. Probably it was then she'd made up her mind to bring Cree back, whatever the cost.

"He's a good, solid man, Ezra is," her mother said now. "I'm not so worried as I was. I hope you're going to listen to him before doing anything wild."

"I'm glad you like him," Pawnee said, avoiding a direct answer.

"Just let me tell you, Pawnee, it won't make up for losing Cree if we lose you, too," her mother said now, with that knack she sometimes had for reading her daughter's mind. "I know you've got something in your head, I know you're not telling us everything. Don't you do anything stupid out there. You're too used to saving Cree from herself, but this time you should accept that you just can't."

Pawnee coughed over the frog in her throat and went quickly to the door. "Yeah, I hear you, Mom."

"Do you? I hope so," her mother spoke to her back. "You don't know how much your father loves you, Pawnee. He can't say it out loud, but he's always been as proud of you as could be. It broke his heart to lose the farm before he could pass it on to you. And it'll kill him if we lose you. You're not just his favourite, Pawnee. You're his life now. Remember that, and come back safe."

Her throat was too tight. It wasn't like her mother to talk this way. She could only nod.

Miranda had organized everything, including the detail that Sam would go to Ben's for the two days before their departure while Ezra and Pawnee stayed in her apartment. Once that plan was in place it had been impossible to formulate another one. The only

alternative now was for either Pawnee or Ezra to go
to a hotel secretly. But although neither of them said
so, they both knew that the sooner they got used to
living together, the better.

Still, Pawnee was wishing they'd made some other
arrangement just for this night. Their wedding night.

Her parents left, and then Ben and Sam, who would
be back in a couple of hours to take them out to
dinner. Of course Sam wanted to see her brother on
his last free night in Toronto, but Pawnee knew that
they were also trying to save her and Ezra from the
awkwardness of that post-wedding meal alone. In a
real marriage, tonight's meal would have been full of
anticipation and happiness. But Ezra was looking at
her with a hollow-eyed look that only made her feel
guilty.

She was feeling pretty down herself. Ever since
he'd agreed to marry her, she'd had her doubts about
what she was doing. Suppose her plan didn't work?
Suppose, as her mother said, it only meant that she
and Cree were both lost? Suppose what she planned
somehow got Ezra fired in spite of her precautions?
She would hate that. He was a kind, loving guy, a
gentle giant. She would hate it if through her actions
his generosity was the ruin of his career.

''Do you want coffee or something?'' she asked,
as Ezra came back into the apartment now and closed
the door.

He stood leaning with his back against the door,
looking at her. There was a long moment of silence.
His face was unreadable. Nervously Pawnee fingered
the unfamiliar weight of the gold band on her finger.

''No, I don't want coffee, thanks,'' he said at last.

He straightened and began to pull off his tie. They were both still in their wedding clothes.

"I'm used to the sofa," Ezra said. "You better have the bedroom. I've put your bags in there."

She took that as the signal for her to leave him. Pawnee didn't argue. "I guess I'll change," she said.

It had been a mistake, Ezra reflected later that evening, to think that dinner with Sam and Ben would somehow take the heat out of the situation. If he'd thought about it for a year, he'd never have said he would start to feel funny about a woman just because he'd put a ring on her finger. He couldn't understand it. And being in company was not going to ease matters. Not this particular company, at any rate.

For a start, his sister glowed. He didn't think he'd ever seen Sam so happy since they were kids. He knew that was due to Ben; there was nothing like love to make a woman beautiful, and she sure had never been like this around that cold stick she'd been seeing previously.

Irrationally, he found it irritating that *he* didn't make *Pawnee* look like that. Their marriage had solved a big problem for her, but she was still drawn and tense, and he could see there was something worrying her. Well, he'd always suspected she had some plan in mind for when she got to Shams, and he supposed the closer it got, the more nervous she was going to be. He would have to keep a very sharp eye on her, to prevent her doing something that was dangerous.

On the one hand, he wished he hadn't done it. On the other, it annoyed him that the woman he'd just married looked as though she'd received a sentence of death by firing squad. Dammit, she was his *wife*.

His body stirred at the thought. Ezra jumped. Damnation! What was the matter with him, anyway? This was something he didn't need!

Well, he didn't have far to look for the cause. The air between Ben and his sister was practically smoking. He'd seen guys get it bad before, but never with quite Ben's heat. As he watched, Sam reached out and put her hand on her fiancé's, smiling into his eyes as she spoke. The muscles in Ben's jaw tightened, and his eyelids came down to hide his eyes. Maybe no one saw it but Ezra, but he knew Ben was fighting for control. When he lifted his lids again and looked at Sam, there was still way too much feeling there. Sam caught her breath and looked away.

Meanwhile, the mean average temperature at the table had jumped by two degrees.

Pawnee was wearing her hair drawn back behind her head, which was a change he could have done without. Up till now it had always looked a bit straggly, falling loosely to just below her chin, and tonight he noticed the bone structure of her face for the first time: strong cheekbones, a small, firm chin. She was wearing makeup, too; he didn't think she'd done that before. The result was that she looked somehow remote. Sexy but unattainable, and wrapped up in her own thoughts. No reason that should annoy him, but it did.

He'd thought before that she was probably too thin, but that had been guesswork, because she'd always been wearing layers of baggy sweaters and loose jeans. Tonight, dressed in a slim black dress and jacket that he knew she'd borrowed from Sam, she took all the guesswork out of it. She *was* too thin, but the surprise was, she had a very curvy body. The slightly protruding bones of hips, neck and wrist couldn't hide the natural roundness of that little butt, nor the long, smooth, undulating line of thigh, knee, calf and ankle. Nor the faint shadow between the small, high breasts...

His body was hard before he knew it, pressing uncomfortably against his belly and the fabric of his shorts. Ezra grabbed for the wine bottle and filled everybody's glass again before taking a good hefty slug of his own. Damn, damn, damn!

Pawnee shifted uncomfortably and crossed her legs again as Ezra eyed her thigh under the too-short dress. She knew he was thinking it didn't suit her, and he was right, but she'd packed only hot-weather clothes and sent all her winter stuff home with her parents. Sam had assured her that she could supply her with a wardrobe for the two days before they left town.

Yesterday Sam had taken her next door to her neighbour, Marie. Marie was a model who had an extensive wardrobe in three sizes, for when her weight fluctuated. She had pulled out a few things for Pawnee to choose from, most of them wildly extreme, but this little black outfit among them. Pawnee, thinking the dress was a long skirt, had opted for it. When she'd discovered her mistake, earlier tonight, of course she wasn't going to go knocking on Marie's door to demand something else.

Raised on the farm, Pawnee had never worried too much about things like clothes. The only time she ever wore a skirt was to go and talk to her father's bank manager. At waitressing jobs and the other work she'd had since the bankruptcy, mostly they let women wear pants, and that was what the wardrobe she was taking to Shamsirabia consisted of: baggy cotton pants and loose shirts, not too far from what a lot of Eastern women wore.

So she wasn't used to the feeling of thin black tights as her only leg covering, nor a tiny, clinging little dress that rode up practically to her hips however she sat. She had to go to the toilet, but that meant getting across the restaurant, and for all she knew the dress might ride right up to her waist when she walked. She just couldn't make the trek alone.

At last Sam picked up her bag and excused herself, then looked with a smile and raised eyebrows at her new sister-in-law. Pawnee stood up and went with her.

"Gosh, this outfit of your friend's is so tight!" she exclaimed, the moment they were safe inside the ladies' room. She stood in front of the full-length mirror. The top was low-cut, too, but at least the jacket covered her arms and most of her chest. Pawnee pulled at the dress hem. "Don't you think it's too small for me?"

Sam looked surprised. "Is it?" She turned to look into the mirror at Pawnee's reflection. "You look great. Is it uncomfortable?"

"But it's so short!"

Sam laughed. She was a couple of inches taller than Pawnee, and side by side with her, her own skirt was two inches shorter, which meant they were more or less exactly the same length. Pawnee followed the direction of her gaze and laughed, too.

"I guess I've never got used to city fashion," she muttered. "Do I really look all right?"

"You look like a model. You remind me of Marie when she's dressed to kill, except you're not so waif-like. Marie sometimes looks starved. You just look elegant."

Pawnee blinked and turned back to examine her reflection with new eyes. "No one ever told me *that* before. I'm sure your brother thinks it's too short."

"Well, you're his wife now. Maybe he doesn't like the way all the men are looking at you."

For no reason at all, Pawnee felt her cheeks go hot. "Nobody's looking at me," she protested. "And if they did, why would Ezra mind?"

Sam shrugged and grinned. "You tell me," she said.

They drove back to Sam's place in silence in the car that Ezra's company had loaned him while he was in Toronto. They had parted with Sam and Ben at the restaurant. Both of them wanted the other couple to come back with them, but there would have been no sense in it. There was far too much to do tomorrow to make this a late night.

It was snowing hard. "Sure hope this doesn't keep up," Ezra muttered, switching on the windscreen wipers as the fat, soft flakes flattened themselves against the windscreen with little kisses of abandon.

"It's been a snowy winter."

That was all they said, all the way back to Sam's. But it wasn't like those other times when he'd felt speechless around a woman. This was different. Usually he just didn't have anything at all to say. Tonight his head was buzzing with things he might have said, if only he could make sense of them. But he had the feeling that even if he could, nothing he was thinking was a safe topic of conversation.

Pawnee wasn't wearing boots, and by the time he'd pulled up in front of Sam's building the streets were two inches deep in snow. "Boy, I was dumb," she said, looking out at the pristine white blanket.

"I'd better carry you inside," Ezra said, before he thought. "Otherwise you'll ruin your shoes."

He came round to her door, and she stood up on the edge of the car floor and wrapped an arm around his neck. Her coat fell away and his arm slid under her legs against nylon-covered skin.

She was light, and he was big. Pawnee took the keys, and closed and locked the car while he held her, trying to ignore the pressure of his arm and hand against her thigh. Then he strode through the falling snow towards the building's main door.

Her thigh was warm against his hand, her breath fanned his neck…and if he'd wanted to kiss her, there was no way she could have stopped him, Ezra told himself. He was suddenly aware of his own size, in a way he hadn't been since he was sixteen.

As soon as they were inside the outer door, Ezra dumped Pawnee on her feet. But his hand caught on the hem of her skirt, pulling it up till she felt nearly naked. Awkwardly, muttering his apologies, he disentangled himself from her coat, pulled out Sam's keys and unlocked the inner door. Pawnee pulled her skirt down without looking at him.

An elevator had never been so small, or so slow. Ezra's blood was overreacting to the quick changes in temperature, or to something. Pawnee stared at the floor, fiddling with a strand of hair that had come loose from the twist of black silk flowers that held it back, and for the first time he understood why men kissed women's hands.

The alarm beeped as they entered the apartment, and Pawnee stepped across the hall to key in the number. Ezra shrugged out of his coat and hung it up, then took his wife's from her. His wife's.

A hallway had never been so small, and it wasn't going anywhere, either. For an impossibly long moment they stood there, feeling how close the space was, discovering how fast a heart could beat.

Then, looking at nothing, she whispered a goodnight. He almost reached for her as she went by. Almost. But it wasn't part of the deal. He remembered her saying, ''Anything,'' when she was begging to marry him, and thought that she might give in just to keep him happy, keep him to the deal. He sure didn't want that.

The bedroom door closed softly, shutting off his thoughts.

When he undressed, of course he was hard again. Damn, damn, damn.

When she awoke the room had a pale glow that she immediately understood the significance of. Pawnee jumped up and ran to pull open the blind onto a world of white. There was snow everywhere, at least a foot had fallen in the night, and it was still coming down. The city was silent.

A glance told her the bathroom was empty, and she grabbed her clothes and the towel Sam had left for her and tiptoed in to have a shower. As she passed the sitting room she heard the sound of the television, so she assumed Ezra was awake.

She was quick. When she emerged there was the smell of coffee in the air that drew her inexorably to the door of the living room.

"Hi," she said.

Ezra, dressed in blue jeans and a denim shirt, was on the sofa, the telephone in one hand, a cup of coffee in the other, the television control beside him. The volume was turned down. On the screen someone was talking about the weather. At the corner of the screen a tiny clock informed her it was two minutes to eight.

Of course, he would be worried about whether their flight would get off tomorrow if this kept up. There were a lot of formalities to get through today, too, and if the roads were impassable that might be difficult.

He nodded at her, just as someone obviously picked up the phone at the other end. "Ted?" Ezra said into the mouthpiece. "Ez here. Have you been following this?" He paused. Pawnee wandered into the kitchen and poured herself a cup of coffee to the background of his urgent speech. "Yeah, yeah, yeah. Nope, I haven't heard anything except what's been on the news. I can't raise Norm yet." He paused, listening. Pawnee was a little surprised by the urgency in his voice. Surely the delay of a day or two in departure wasn't such a big deal?

"I don't know, Ted, it looks pretty bloody bad to me. Yeah, my nose says this is it. Hold on."

The signature tune of the eight o'clock news was playing softly as she returned to the sitting room, and she sank into a comfortable armchair as Ezra put down his cup and, picking up the remote, punched the volume up.

"Good morning. First, the headlines," said the announcer, and it was only as Ezra sat forward in close attention, the phone resting against his powerful chest, that it belatedly dawned on Pawnee that something more serious had happened than bad weather.

"The palace and government buildings in the capital of Shamsirabia have apparently been attacked and taken over by Islamic rebels of the Hezbuddin faction late last night. Early unconfirmed reports suggest that the uprising may have been successful.

"The prime minister is due to return today from..."

The sound disappeared again, and Ezra started talking into the phone. Pawnee sat staring at the silent screen with the wide, blank gaze of a stone statue. Then, with the slow precision of the horror-struck, she turned to look at Ezra. He was a stranger, a total stranger. And less than twenty-four hours ago she had married him. Pawnee didn't need to be told that her marriage was now useless to her. But she had promised Ezra...what had she promised?

5

Never in her life had she done so little while so much was happening around her, Pawnee reflected more than once over the hours and days that followed.

Shamsirabia was rocked with revolution, the oil-consuming nations of the world were feeling the tips of their spears, the mosque project was cancelled, and all Pawnee could do was sit on the sofa in front of Sam's television and listen to the same know-nothing news reports on the twenty-four-hour news channels, hour after hour. She couldn't even go home to her parents, who naturally expected her to remain with her new husband.

For two days the world knew nothing beyond the most basic information: something was happening, or had happened, in Shamsirabia.

"No news so far of Cree Walker, the young Canadian hostage who has been held by the very faction that is apparently behind the coup," the newsman admitted, for the fifteenth time that day, and in a sudden eruption of feeling, Pawnee punched the remote. With satisfaction she watched the screen blacken to a pinpoint of light, watched it pink out. So. She did

have some control over events after all. She could turn off the damned television.

She got up and wandered into the kitchen to pour herself a cup of coffee. She was getting used to Sam's pleasant little apartment. It was homey. Maybe she'd made a mistake, after the crash of the farm, not forcing herself to settle and find a place like this to make a home. For almost two years now she'd been living a rover's life, taking live-in work in this or that hotel, up in cottage country during the season, at the ski hills in winter. Probably it was time she made some decisions.

She was very carefully not looking at the fact that Ezra would now play a part in any decision she made. That thought was never very far from consciousness, but Pawnee was getting very good at pushing it out of her mind. When she thought of the promises she might have made in the depths of her desperation...what if he held her to them?

He couldn't. He wouldn't. Anyway, she'd made them under duress. She was pretty sure that legally any promise made under duress didn't count.

The phone rang. She almost dropped the coffeepot, but saved it in time, slammed it down on the table in a spreading coffee puddle and dashed into the living room.

"Hi. It's Ez."

She clutched the receiver. She could hear from his voice that he had news. "Ezra, what's happened?"

"It's good news. Are you sitting down?"

Pawnee felt her knees give way under her, and she landed on the sofa. "I'm sitting," she whispered.

"We're pretty sure Cree's been released. As far as

we know, the Polygon company plane is bringing her out with our advance team. We think the plane has already taken off and is flying to the Emirates. We may not get more news, or real confirmation, till they land.''

She was crying, the tears streaming uncontrollably down her cheeks, all the tears she hadn't allowed herself to weep since the first announcement that Cree was a hostage. ''Oh, thank God, Ezra! Thank God! Oh, isn't it marvellous, wonderful news!''

''Polygon's been working on getting our advance team out. Apparently Cree was brought to the airport and released, and our plane was there ready to go and the pilot just agreed to take her. We haven't released that information to the media yet.''

She was sobbing too much to speak coherently. ''Oh, thank the pilot when you talk to him! Thank them all for me!'' she babbled. ''Ezra, should I phone Mom and Dad now?''

He breathed. ''Do you want to wait till we get our first word from the pilot? As soon as he's out of Shamsirabian airspace we can be a little more sure of what's really happened. You know how these things are, Pawnee, it may all be—'' He broke off, not wanting to say it. ''Nothing's certain,'' he said instead.

''Yes, all right. Yes, maybe that's best. Will you call me as *soon* as you hear? I'd like to tell them before they hear it on the news.''

''I promise, Pawnee,'' Ezra said gently.

The next hours were intolerable. Never had Pawnee felt so useless. All she could do was pace and hope. Sam came over to keep her company, as she had so often during the past few tense days; of course Ezra had phoned his sister to tell her the good news. The two women sat together, watching what news there was, alternately feeling certain that it must be true and worrying that someone had got it wrong.

After an intolerable wait, the company jet pilot talked to air traffic controllers in neutral territory, and Ezra phoned to say that it was true. Cree had been released, and was definitely aboard the Polygon company jet en route for Riyadh.

"Of course the Saudi air traffic control has notified the media along with us," Ezra said, "so I'd better hang up so you can call your parents."

In the end, Pawnee couldn't make herself understood through her tears. It was Sam who gave her mother the news that her daughter was safe and well and apparently unharmed. Two minutes later, it was a simultaneous newsflash on the Newsworld channel and on CCN, as well as being flashed along the bottom of the screen on all the networks.

"*Hostage Cree Walker, whose fate has captured the hearts and minds of Canadians since she was kidnapped from a Shamsirabian market four weeks ago, has now been released,*" said the anchorwoman, in satisfied tones. "*She is understood to be in a Canadian Forces plane en route for Istanbul, and is due to land there in approximately three hours…*"

Sam and Pawnee were hugging each other, alternately laughing and crying with relief. "Boy, it just shows you, doesn't it?" Sam said, wiping her eyes. "You always believe exactly what the news tells you, but they sure don't have that right."

"Well, I don't care if she's in a Zeppelin heading for Reykjavik, as long as she's out of there," Pawnee said, and then they burst into the uncontrollable, tearful laughter of relief again.

Barney McNab, the powerful head of Canadian Cable News, sent his own company jet out from London to Riyadh to meet the Polygon flight and bring Cree Walker home to a panting nation. His top woman reporter, by chance in London on another story, was on board, as was a crack British medical team sent to check Cree over and, of course, a television crew.

The next thing the world heard, exclusively on CCN, was an interview, carried from the plane by satellite, between the top woman journalist and an excited, bouncing, irrepressible Cree. She had not been hurt. She had not been kept in isolation. She had never been seriously ill.

By the time Ezra got home, both Pawnee and her parents had talked privately to Cree, courtesy of CCN telephone hookups in the plane. She really was fine.

Listening to the interview for the tenth time when she heard the key in the lock, Pawnee flew up off the sofa and, without pausing for thought, straight into Ezra's arms.

"Oh, Ezra, isn't it wonderful? Oh, how lucky that your company plane was there! Did you tell them how grateful I am?"

"Great news," he agreed. He wrapped his arms tightly around her, overwhelming her with his size, and she shivered and was abruptly nervous. Did he think she was—

"You're *freezing!*" she exclaimed, in case he had misunderstood the shiver. So Ezra let her go to take off and hang up his cold outer clothes. When he'd done that, she had stepped back out of reach. They stood awkwardly eyeing each other.

"Sam gone?" he asked, to defuse the silence.

"Yes, she's got some assignment and it's all on Ben's computer, so she had to go back to finish it. Do you want coffee or a beer or something?" Pawnee asked.

"Beer would be nice." He stood for a moment rubbing his icy hands for warmth and wishing she didn't sound quite so much like an airline hostess. Then he sank onto the sofa in front of the television, which was running the airplane interview again. "Your sister sounds as though she's been on an Outward Bound adventure instead of in a hostage situation," he observed.

"I know, I know, I think it must be true what she's saying, that they didn't hurt her, or she couldn't sound like that. I mean, she sounded just like herself, even when she was talking to me! Oh, Ezra, thanks so much for everything!" She returned and handed him a glass of neatly poured beer.

"I didn't do anything." He smiled at her and drank gratefully. "It would have happened the same if I'd never met you. The pilot who made the decision didn't know we were married. He just made the humane decision. He broke some laws, of course. Cree has no papers or exit visa or anything. Another man might have worried about protecting his own butt and left her there."

"I think he should get the Order of Canada medal."

He grinned at her, liking the fact that she so obviously loved her sister, could express it so freely. He could see she'd make a good mother. A good wife, too, whenever she got around to marrying a guy she loved. She had loyalty. No man she loved would ever have cause to worry... Ezra decided to stop thinking along those lines.

Later, over a dinner she had cooked, there was room for other considerations. Pawnee asked, "Is the mosque project definitely cancelled?"

Ezra nodded. "Definitely. They've started to reassign the team already."

"What are we going to do, Ezra?"

He chewed a delicious bite of some vegetable concoction he'd never tasted before. She'd been right about that, for sure. She could make it as a cook anywhere.

"I don't know," he admitted uncomfortably. He was reluctant to talk about it, without really knowing why. They would have to think of a way out, and probably the sooner they started, the better.

"Isn't it weird, though? If we'd only delayed twenty-four hours...in fact, if we'd been getting married at City Hall, we'd have had to wait till Monday! Because we let Miranda arrange it all, we ended up married *one day* before it became unnecessary. When you *think* of the coincidence!"

He was annoyed, without knowing why. "Miranda says there's no such thing as coincidence."

She just blinked. "Ezra, what are we going to do?"

"Let's not worry about it right now. Let's get your sister home first. You've got enough worries."

"But won't it be best if we decide on some story

right away? You know, maybe you could tell your boss we cancelled the wedding.''

Now he knew why he didn't want to talk about it. "I already told him we got married. The guys are taking up a collection for a wedding present.''

"Oh, *no!*'' said Pawnee, putting down her fork.

He didn't see why she had to look so tragic about it. "Well, it's kinda nice of them, don't you think?''

"But—Ezra, how are you going to explain?''

"How am I going to explain what?''

"Well, I mean, you'll be going on an assignment soon, won't you? And won't they expect...?''

He went kind of quiet, and she nervously stopped speaking. The silence hung there for a bit. Then he spoke.

"You've already decided what we're going to do, is that it?'' he asked levelly.

She was startled. What else was there to be done? "Well, for goodness' sake, you don't—''

"You've got what you wanted, all promises are off, is that what I hear?''

She stared at him. "Well, what do you expect?'' She'd never seen him like this before. Usually Ezra seemed gentle, almost placid. Suddenly his presence seemed to fill the room.

"I expect a little more thought to be given to the thing before you take off leaving me holding the baby,'' he said flatly.

"What baby? What's happened?'' she asked in confusion. It had never occurred to her in a million Sundays that he might want her to— "You said you're going to be reassigned! I can't just go with you.''

"You mean you won't."

That wasn't what she meant at all, and Pawnee felt a little bullet of anger shoot her heart. "I must say I think it's pretty selfish of *you* if you're expecting me to go on with this pretence now! I'm supposed to put my life on hold and go to some godforsaken, fly-infested hole with you for months on end while you build a bridge? And why? Just to save your ego with your buddies?"

"I never said that!" he half shouted.

"You implied it, though, didn't you? The fact that my life's been rudely derailed and I'd like to get it back on track is nothing, compared to the fact that if we split up now people might think we didn't get along in bed on our wedding night."

"They would think one helluva lot more than that, and you know it."

"Oh, right! What would they think, at the worst? That you're impotent? That you're some kind of deviant and pervert? What would be worse for a guy's reputation among the guys? That you were a sexual monster?"

I hope you behaved yourself tonight, Ezra.

"They might think you were frigid," he countered, with a flat coldness that shook her. "Or that you'd deliberately manipulated me into marriage in order to be near your sister. Or—" his voice dropped and he spoke slowly, as if for a moral or mental midget "—they might think I'd been prepared to violate employer-employee trust by engaging in a fraud that could have put Polygon in serious trouble if the information had gotten out and the company was thought to be involved."

Pawnee was not normally an unreasonable woman, but the tone of his voice blinded her to the justice of what he said. "Oh, don't be ridiculous!" she exploded, even while something at the back of her mind murmured that Ezra had a point.

"Ah, I see." He nodded at her with his face absolutely closed. "It's been a one-way street from the start. You never had any intention of keeping your word. You were going to hit the road as soon as your sister's fate was decided, and be damned to what that meant for me. It was a manipulative little plan that had every intention of sacrificing me."

"It was *not!*"

"You never meant to keep your word, did you?"

She didn't answer, couldn't answer, when he put it in that cold, level, accusing way that was going to make the worst of whatever she said.

"Did you?"

"I wasn't going to break it in the way you mean!"

He laughed, a real laugh, throwing back his head and showing his teeth, like some fine, wild, dangerous animal with a glossy pelt, she thought inconsequently. "But you were going to break it," he insisted.

Again she could not reply.

"Come on, Pawnee, let's have the truth!" he said, in rough impatience. He felt humiliated. He'd guessed she had some plan, but he had trusted her word; he had never once doubted it. "You're not a coward, after all! Let's hear it! What was your real plan?"

Goaded, she said what she had never meant to tell anyone. "I wasn't just going to walk out on you, Ezra! If you must know, I was going to—I was going to offer them a trade. Me for Cree."

The words sat there in the silence, flat and rubbery, congealing like fried eggs on a plate, while he stared at her in complete and numbing disbelief. He was experiencing the most confusing mix of emotions he hoped he'd ever feel in his life. He could not have begun to say what was uppermost.

"How in the hell were you going to manage that?" he demanded softly after a full minute.

"I had—I have the rebels' code word. Somebody in External Affairs let it slip one day while we were talking. Basically, I knew how to get in touch with them secretly."

"And you were—" He broke off, too angry to continue, and took a deep, deep breath. He put down his knife and fork and pressed his eyes and forehead with his hands, as if he might be able to drive comprehension into his brain physically. He muttered a short, emphatic string of expletives that startled her, and then looked at her again.

"I could shake you," he observed conversationally.

In spite of his words, there was no threat of physical violence in him. She was not afraid of that. But behind his level tones there was deep anger, and that did make her nervous.

"I don't see why—what did it have to do with you?"

His jaw tightened, and he turned his head away and then back. "What did it have to do with me?" he repeated incredulously, and immediately she wished she hadn't said those words. Of course it would have affected him, though perhaps she had not given

enough consideration to just how much. "What did
it..."

And then suddenly they were shouting at each other
in a full-scale fight that was unlike either of them.
The fact that Pawnee felt guiltily in the wrong did not
stop the angry tirade of defensiveness that rose in her.
It only added emphasis. The fact that Ezra's first reaction was horror at the thought of what the success
of her plot might have meant for her rather than for
him didn't stop him berating her for her betrayal of
their agreement.

They tore each other's character, motives, morals
and origins into shreds, each amazed at the strength
of their own and the other's anger, each blind as to
what fuelled it.

"Right! You can *have* your divorce!" Ezra shouted
in the end. "I wouldn't want to take you with me to
the end of the *street*, let alone someplace where I'd
be locked up with you as my only entertainment night
after night!"

"I always *knew* you saw women in that kind of
sexist, drivelling way!" Pawnee countered. "I am not
your *entertainment!*"

"You don't need to tell me that! I'd rather see
Gone With the Goddamn Wind for the hundred and
second time than count on you for amusement!"

"What you need," she pointed out sweetly, "is
one of Miranda's brainless, chesty blondes. I'm
amazed you didn't let her arrange something for
you."

"I didn't let her arrange something for me because
I was too damn busy playing Sir Galahad for you and

your sister!'' he pointed out explosively. ''Which is a mistake I won't be so quick to make again!''

''And poor you! Now you'll have nobody to entertain you with her mindless chitterings during those hot, dry nights. Well, I am sorry! Maybe if I go to Miranda and tell her it turns out I've got too much brain for your comfort, she can find someone in a hurry before you're assigned again.''

He looked at her. ''You don't have too much brain, Pawnee,'' he said, in a voice that made her cringe and hear what she had just said. ''You have not enough conscience. And you don't have to worry about me dragging you to any godforsaken hellhole to save my reputation or for any other reason.''

The worst of it was, when it was all over, neither of them had anywhere else to go. They had to share a bathroom, marching past each other in stony silence. They had to settle down for sleep only yards from each other, knowing sleep would be impossible. They had to toss and turn, listening to the other toss and turn through the bedroom wall.

They had to regret what they had said, without any possibility of creeping into the bed of the other in the darkness and whispering, ''Sorry.''

''Well, Ez!'' said Norm, striding into his office. Flinging himself down in the big black leather chair, he tossed a file folder on the desk. Ezra had been sitting there only a minute, waiting, but it hadn't been a pleasant minute. Whatever he had said to Pawnee last night, this was not a situation he relished explaining. He could feel sweat all over his scalp.

''Norm,'' he said, nodding.

"Great news about your sister-in-law! Wish I could be there myself to see her welcomed home! Sounds like it's going to be a real party at the SkyDome. They say CCN is laying on champagne for the whole crowd."

"They sure know how to make a news event," Ezra agreed, a little dryly. Things didn't seem quite the same when you'd been privy to all the behind-the-scenes arrangements.

"Guess your wife's out at the airport, is she? You didn't go?"

No, he hadn't gone, and Norm would know why soon enough. But Ezra just shook his head.

"I guess you've heard the rumours going around and wanted to get in quick, and I can't say I blame you, though as it turns out, you could have left it to me." Ezra blinked. "It's true—thank God nothing serious, as you probably heard. It's a broken leg. It's enough to keep him out of commission for a while, but there shouldn't be any complications."

Ezra grinned helplessly. "Norm, I'm in the dark here."

His boss looked up from the papers he was shuffling in surprise. "You aren't here because of Gerry's accident?"

"Hell, no! Gerry had an accident? I'm sorry to hear that. What happened?"

Norm hesitated, rubbing his face. "Welllll...that's just what we don't know. You know there's been a certain hostility to that hotel project on Kaha Akua. Ger says he's pretty sure it was a genuine accident, but we can't rule out sabotage. You maybe want to think about that awhile, because of course it means taking your wife out there.''

Ezra stared at him. ''What are you saying, Norm?'' he said slowly.

His boss lifted his hands, grinning. ''I'm saying that we're ready to look at that promotion to project boss for you and send you to the Hawaii project as Gerry's replacement, Ez. I guess I shouldn't tell you this, but—you only missed it last time because of not being married. Because of the problems with the residents I promised the owner we'd have somebody very stable at the helm, and I'm afraid that means a married man, accompanied by his wife. The men are too inclined to try and run around with the local girls out there as it is, and we want someone able to keep them in line a bit.'' Norm rubbed his nose. ''Couldn't tell you that before, of course. Have you looking for a wife for all the wrong reasons. But that's what's held you back from a couple of jobs you wanted, Ez. And now that you've gone and got yourself a wife, you can look on Hawaii as yours. If you want it, of course!''

He chuckled, then looked at Ezra's half-amazed, half-horrified face with some surprise. ''Maybe you'd better go home and discuss it with your wife, Ezra,'' he said dryly. ''A six-month honeymoon on The Spirit Isle might not be every bride's cup of tea.''

And then he laughed loudly, as though he'd just told a joke.

6

The bad weather in Peterborough had escalated into a blizzard overnight, and not even Barney McNab could do anything about getting a limousine through to pick up the homecoming hostage's parents.

"To tell you the truth, we don't really mind," Chris Walker said to her daughter over the phone at six that morning, when it was absolutely clear that there was no way for them to get through even to the train station. "Your father and I won't enjoy all that fuss at the Dome and with the television cameras. We're quite happy to wait for Cree here, where we can talk to her in private. You go, Pawnee."

So she went in solitary splendour to the airport, and the next few hours passed in a daze. She and Cree had a dreamlike hour alone in one cabin in the CCN plane, where they mostly just hugged and cried. Then CCN took over.

Later, she would watch it all on television, but Pawnee hardly had any independent memory of what happened. Appearing at the top of the plane steps for a "photo-op", just behind a wildly waving and grinning Cree. The ride in the limousine with Cree and the famous CCN reporter, arrival at the nearly packed stadium in the centre of the city with a crowd cheering as though they wanted to deafen the world with their joy. Speeches and tears…and then at last, Cree, who had been firm about what she would and wouldn't do throughout, saying, "I'm going home with my sister now, to be normal for a bit."

That was the last of the soundbites. After that, CCN had responded to Cree's wishes. In an ordinary car the two women had been secretly driven away from the Dome, while a couple of limousines had gone the other way, followed by the cars of the press.

Only CCN knew where they were staying, and they certainly wouldn't be telling anybody.

And at last, in the back seat of the three-year-old Ford wagon, Pawnee felt like herself again. And remembered that she had almost as much explaining to do as Cree had.

"My gosh, you've lost more weight than I have!" Cree exclaimed, as Pawnee slipped off her coat and hung it in Sam's closet. With things the way they were, it seemed really outrageous that she and Ezra were still sharing Sam's place, but the blizzard in Peterborough meant there was nowhere else to go. Sam had insisted that Pawnee take Cree to her place.

"Yeah, well, we were very worried," Pawnee said simply. "There didn't seem to be time to eat. Not that there was anything we could really do, except phone Ottawa every five minutes."

"What's *that?*" her sister shrieked. She grabbed Pawnee's left hand and lifted it up. It had been easy enough to slip the ring off with her gloves earlier, but just now she'd forgotten. "Is that a wedding ring? Are you *married?* Who *to,* for goodness' sake?"

Well, it had to be explained.

Sensing Pawnee's hesitation, Cree shifted her gaze up into her sister's face.

"Um…yeah, I have to talk to you about that," Pawnee began awkwardly, leading her into the sitting room. "You're going to find it a bit incredible, so could you just listen till I've finished? Otherwise it'll take all day."

And Cree curled up in one corner of Sam's sofa, crossed her hands in her lap, tilted her dark head in the way she always did when she was curious, and said, as she always did, "Consider me a large ear."

The tears started in Pawnee's eyes as she flung her arms around her sister. "Oh, I'm so glad to have you back! You don't know how we worried! I was so afraid of what they might be doing to you… We never knew whether to believe we'd ever see you again."

Cree tearfully returned the embrace. "Yeah, I can just about imagine. I think." They sat back. "And does that have something to do with why you got married?"

Considering all the complications, it took a surprisingly short time to tell her sister everything about the past few weeks. As good as her word, Cree listened, hardly saying anything, her facial expressions detailing her reactions. Her eyes went wide, her mouth opened, she even clapped both hands over her mouth.

"He said yes?" she interjected once. "Boy! Is he crazy, or just really, really nice?"

Pawnee didn't answer, but went steadily on. It wasn't an easy story to tell.

"But I don't understand what you were going to do once you got there! What could you do in Shamsirabia that you couldn't do right here?" Cree said at last.

Pawnee shifted uncomfortably. "I told you, I just wanted to be there on the scene. We were sure we weren't getting all the news—"

But Cree interrupted, shaking her head determinedly. "Honey, I know you, right? I've known you all my life. You hate not being able to do anything, and you'd only have hated it more on the spot. So you were going out there with a plan of action, otherwise you wouldn't have gone. What was it?"

"I told you, we—"

"And it was a really dangerous plan, or you'd be telling me about it right now. What was it going to be, Pawnee, a David and Jonathan thing? You were going to offer them a trade or something?"

Pawnee opened her mouth, but the lie wouldn't come, and now it was Cree who had tears in her eyes. "Honestly, honestly!" she said. "Pawnee, how could you come up with such an idea? What made you think I'd allow the exchange? And what if it hadn't worked? What if they'd just grabbed you, too?"

"I thought if they were keeping you in solitary—they do that a lot, don't they?—there was a chance at least that they might put us together, and that would have been an improvement, wouldn't it?"

"For me, maybe. What about Mom and Dad? Don't you know that it would have killed Daddy? Are you telling me they agreed to all this?"

"No, that's the important thing. I didn't tell them, they think we got married because we're in love. Mom suspects something, though, so you have to pretend you don't know anything if she starts to ask you."

"Do they like Ezra?"

"I think Dad approves of him. You know those looks Dad used to give a guy we were dating, and we all knew he thought he wasn't much of a man?"

"Yeah, Pete! And Mike." Cree laughed. "In fact, nearly every guy I ever dated."

"Well, he never looked at Ezra at all like that. He just shook his hand real hard and patted his elbow."

"Really? Daddy gave Ezra his man-to-man handshake? Oh, wow! Pawnee, you better hang onto this guy! When do I get to meet him?"

Pawnee shifted uncomfortably. "Well, that's the other thing. I don't know whether he'll come home or—"

"Home! Are you living here with him?" Up to now, she'd let Cree believe this was just a friend's place she'd borrowed for the occasion.

"Yeah, this is his sister's place."

Cree's eyes were saucers. "Do you sleep with him?"

"No, of course not!" Pawnee said irritably.

"Well, sorry, but how was I to know? The whole thing's so weird, who could guess?"

"Never mind that now. I haven't told you everything yet. We had a big fight last night and agreed to a divorce. Of course I haven't told Mom and Dad yet."

Cree just stared at her. "Boy, and I thought *I* was having an exciting time!"

Ezra almost felt like knocking, but it was stupid when he had the key. Anyway, it was his own sister's apartment. But he hadn't spoken to Pawnee since the last heated words of their argument, and he felt awkward just walking in on her when she wouldn't be expecting him.

She was in the kitchen, doing dishes with the radio turned low. He stood in the doorway, still in his coat. "Hi," he said.

Pawnee whirled, and a plate slipped between her soapy hands and splashed back into the water. "Oh, Ezra! You startled me," she said, blushing.

"Sorry," he muttered. They looked at each other in awkward silence.

"Your sister all right?" he asked.

"Yes, she's in the bedroom sleeping off the biggest meal I've ever seen anyone eat," Pawnee told him, trying to smile. He could see her happiness in having her sister safe was all damped down by his presence, and he found this annoying. Dammit, he'd married her to save her sister! It was a Polygon plane that had got her out! Didn't she—

He pushed down this irrational nonsense, but at least it had given him the anger he needed to tell her.

"Look, about last night…"

Pawnee bit her lip and rushed into speech. "Yes, Ezra, I'm sorry about being so—"

"Well, good," he interrupted. "Because what I said about a divorce isn't a deal. I just got offered a posting in Hawaii." He hadn't planned on telling her so abruptly, but he was afraid he wouldn't say it at all unless he said it right now.

"Oh, that's nice."

"Very nice. The only fly in the ointment is, the offer's only open if I have a wife. And guess what, Pawnee—you're it."

They had had another raging argument, no less angry because it had been carried on in subdued voices to keep from waking Cree. They had gotten nowhere. Ezra had stormed out of the apartment, only to be driven back again: the blizzard had descended on the city without their noticing. He couldn't see a foot in front of his face. No one would be going anywhere for a while.

"Tell them your wife doesn't want to go to Hawaii! Say it's too hot for me," she had flung at him at one point.

He had snorted furiously. "Tell them that the woman who was very eager to come to Shamsirabia with me won't come because *Hawaii* is too *hot?*" he demanded. "That's as good as telling them I've married a complete lunatic!"

Pawnee tried another tack. "Look, Ezra, please understand. I've been living in a kind of limbo ever since my parents lost the farm. That's almost two years ago now. And then, just when I was getting to the point of thinking I had to make some decisions, Cree was kidnapped, and my life went up in the air again. Now you're saying I should wait another— what, six months? before I decide what to do with my life."

"No, I'm not."

"What are you saying, then?"

"I'm saying what you should decide to do with your life for the next six months is come to Hawaii with me. What's wrong with that?"

She heaved a furious breath. "Right. I should decide to go to Hawaii with you. Is that long-term? Is that any kind of major life decision, Ezra, or am I just putting it off?"

"What's wrong with taking a good long holiday while you decide about your life?"

She fought for calm. "Look, Ezra, I'm sure if we thought about it we could come up with some explanation that would sound just fine. I mean, for example, your employers know I'm Cree's sister, right? Couldn't we just say I want to stay home to be with her for a while and I'll join you later?"

"Yeah, and then what happens?"

"Well, they'll just forget about it eventually."

He rolled his eyes and shook his head in exasperation. "No, they won't just forget about it. I told you, they want a project boss who's married and whose wife is going to be there with him. If you aren't there very damn soon, they're going to start asking questions."

"I can't go. I can't believe you're asking me to."

"When *you* needed a fake marriage, you could believe it, all right."

It had been a relief when Cree finally woke up, the necessity for an introduction putting an end to the argument and their enforced confinement with each other.

"I guess you've told your sister all about it," Ezra said a short time later over dinner.

"Yeah!" Cree said. "Really weird, if you don't mind my saying so!" She looked at Ezra with a friendly grin, trying to ease the atmosphere.

"But I haven't heard any of the details. Where were you being held?"

Cree burst into laughter. "Oh, *me!* Oh, right, yeah, we did talk about that, too! Do you really want to hear about it?" Cree asked.

"If you want to tell," Ezra said. "I know sometimes people don't like to talk about it if it was really...well, it can't have been as good as you said on television, I guess."

She set his mind to rest on that. The heat and lack of food had really been the hardest to put up with. Hezbuddin was a real people's movement and she'd been looked after by village women. Still, Pawnee reflected, it was good for Cree to talk it out again, and Ezra could be a very sympathetic ear when he wasn't being totally selfish and pigheaded. She'd found that out herself over the past few days.

Later, as the two sisters lay side by side in the bedroom, listening to the howl of the wind and the storm as they had so often in a prairie childhood, Cree whispered, "I think you're crazy."

"What?"

"You don't want to go out to Hawaii with that guy? He's lovely. A great big, gentle giant. I'm amazed he hasn't been snapped up before this. Did you say he's twenty-eight?"

"I think women make him really nervous."

"He wasn't nervous of me," Cree said dreamily.

"No, I guess not." Pawnee didn't let herself say, *because you're my sister.*

"I've got a great, great, great idea," Cree said, softly, as though the inspiration were just now being carried to her on the waves of the cosmos.

"What's your great idea?"

"Have you met anybody at Polygon yet? Have you met his boss or anything?"

"No. There hasn't been time. The coup happened on the day we were due to go down to the office."

Cree was nodding happily to herself. "Perfect."

"What?" Pawnee demanded.

"You don't want to go to Hawaii. Ezra needs a wife there. It's simple—I'll pretend to be you and go with him. Frankly, my dear, I'd love to spend six months in romantic Hawaii with your adorable husband. It's the perfect solution, don't you think?"

As it happened, Pawnee *didn't* think so. She thought it was one of the stupidest solutions to anything she'd ever heard, and she couldn't imagine that Ezra would agree. But if he did, it would be fine. It would be just fine with her.

"No," said Ezra flatly.

"Aw," Cree pouted as though she hadn't really expected his agreement. "Don't you like me?" The blizzard had passed. The sunlight, its brightness thrown back at it by the virgin blanket of snow, was pouring blindingly in through the kitchen window as they all three sat at breakfast.

"I like you just fine," he said stonily.

"Well then, it's the perfect solution. Why don't you want to do it?"

He looked at Pawnee. "Do you think it's the perfect solution?" he asked, a little aggrieved. He didn't like the idea of the sisters pawing over him like that, figuring out which one wouldn't mind living with him. It ticked him off that Cree didn't mind, and Pawnee did.

Pawnee shrugged. "It wasn't my idea." And she wasn't sure why she didn't like it. Probably Cree was right, probably it was a good idea. Except that if Pawnee didn't want to put her life on hold for six months, why should Cree do it for her?

"But she's very grateful," Cree interjected. "The thing is, Ezra, Pawnee's a serious-minded woman. You have to understand that. I've always been the fun-loving one, and Pawnee's always been the one who had to face up to responsibility because she was going to inherit the farm. She's a worker. If she'd been the hostage, instead of me, she'd have gone crazy with the inactivity. Or she'd have organized the village so they fixed their well and stuff like that. Me, I just sat around gossiping in sign language with the women who were looking after me.

"The thought of Hawaii just doesn't appeal to Pawnee. Sun and sea and palm trees and piña colada...she'd be hearing my dad's voice all the time, asking her why she wasn't doing her chores. Me, on the other hand, I'm one of those girls who just want to have fun. So—what do you say?"

"It won't work," he said doggedly. He could see that Cree was one of those women who would be wanting him to flirt and play games and all that. But even without that it was a stupid plan.

"Why not?"

"Because everybody and his brother knows damned well who you are!" he pointed out. "Your picture's been all over the place for weeks, you've both been on television for most of yesterday and you're going to be on every talk show going in the next two weeks. How am I supposed to pass you off as the woman I married last Sunday when you were still in Shamsirabia?''

''Oh, pooh! The Americans never follow Canadian news. No one in Hawaii will even know there *was* a hostage in Shamsirabia.''

''Maybe. But my boss is Canadian, and he knows all about it, including the fact that I'm married to Cree Walker's sister.''

''You know what? People aren't that bright. He saw us both together on television, right? If we go in saying I'm Pawnee, he'll never realize. It would be easy enough for me to travel on her passport. We're a lot alike.'' She leaned in towards her sister, putting her face side by side with Pawnee's, and made herself look serious. ''See? Especially now that we're both so thin.''

Ezra looked from one sister to the other. They *were* a lot alike. It might even work, except for Norm. He wondered if there were some way he could avoid having Norm meet ''his wife.'' He shrugged irritably, not sure why he disliked the idea so much. ''I've already got enough to contend with faking that Pawnee's my wife,'' he told Cree. ''I'm damned if on top of that, I'm going to pretend that *you* are *Pawnee*.''

''Suppose we said that you and I were in love all along, and you married Pawnee to take her out there so together you could find a way to get me back? We could make it sound like the love affair of the decade. CCN would love it.''

"Yeah," Ezra said dryly. "How romantic it would be for me to lose my job because I was so in love with my wife's sister."

"They wouldn't fire you for a reason like that! Would they?"

"I'm sure not going to put it to the test."

Pawnee, he noticed, just looked at her plate through it all, shoving the food around, not even pretending to eat. No wonder she was so thin, he told himself, with a spurt of worry. He'd have to feed her up on pineapple and pau pau. In fact, it was a good thing she *was* coming with him, because left to her own devices, she'd probably starve herself into anorexia.

"No," he said flatly. "Your sister made me a promise, and she is going to keep it. And that's that."

7

"You're going to love it!" Miranda said happily as she, Sam, Ezra and Pawnee made their way through the bustling airport crowds to the check-in counter. "Arthur and I spent our honeymoon in Hawaii. Goodness, how many years ago was that? Too many! I wonder if it's all changed? But I'm sure it's still as ravishing now as it was then, at least on Kaha Akua, because it's always been privately owned. And I'm sure Barney McNab hasn't done anything to destroy it since he bought the island. He's not like some," she added distastefully. "He respects nature."

No one responded to this encomium on the environmental sensitivity of Canada's media magnate. "Walking along those beaches at sunset—the moon and the mountains, and the scent of flowers, and the stars!" Miranda went on. "It really is romantic, Pawnee. What a perfect place to start a marriage." She hugged Pawnee's arm in what she dreamed was shared excitement.

Pawnee took a deep breath. If she heard another word about Miranda's honeymoon and how romantic it was all going to be, she'd punch somebody.

She had given in to Ezra in the end. They had argued and shouted about it, but he was right about one thing: she had given her word. She could say what she liked—and she had said a lot—about the fact that the situation had entirely changed, but she *had* promised not to abandon the marriage the moment she was assured of Cree's safely.

She hadn't given in easily. In fact, the more she accepted, inside, that he was right, the louder she argued. She didn't know why. "You said yourself you wouldn't even have *gotten* this promotion if we weren't married!" she had shouted in vain. "You can hardly accuse me of wrecking your career if you *lose* the promotion because we get divorced!"

"I am sick and tired and fed up to the back teeth with the desert!" Ezra had shouted right back. "By sheer good luck it turns out I've got a ticket out, and you're it! You can scream all you want, Pawnee, but you are my wife and *you are coming with me to Hawaii!*"

"And if I don't?"

He'd crossed his arms and glared at her. "Be prepared to be married to me for a good, long time."

"What do you mean by that?" she had demanded furiously.

"I mean just what I say. I'll do everything in the book to prevent you getting a divorce. So if you fall in love with some other man, be prepared to have to crowbar me out of your life before you can make that march to the altar for real!"

Pawnee had stared at him in horror. She had no idea what the divorce laws were; it wasn't something that had ever interested her. She was pretty sure an uncontested divorce took no time, but a *contested* one?

Still, it wasn't that argument that had decided her in the end, though maybe he thought it was. She had given in because she had given him her word, and it was the right thing to do.

But she would *never* forgive him for forcing the issue. He ought to have let her off the hook. He ought to have found some other way. What Pawnee felt now was a huge resentment she couldn't get to grips with, that seethed in her and made her sulky—a mood that was most unlike her.

And Miranda's descriptions of the romantic nights were just about the last straw. She wasn't likely ever to feel romantic about Ezra Jagger, whatever the moon did, she told herself righteously. Perfect place to start a marriage? What she wanted was the perfect place to *end* one.

"Well, I'm dying to come out for a visit," Sam intervened now, and began to chat about how, if they were there long enough, maybe she and Ben would come out for a holiday. Maybe after the wedding, which Ezra and Pawnee had to be sure to come back for.

It was over soon enough, and then they were on the plane looking down on a white, white world, and the last snow they would see for some time, and in her head Pawnee heard Cree's goodbye admonition again, delivered as her irrepressible sister had left for Peterborough, "Don't be an idiot! Do you really want to stay in Toronto for the worst winter of the century? You're on your honeymoon. You go and have a good time—and I mean *a good time!* He is one great guy, and I'd love to be in your shoes.''

Pawnee glanced at Ezra's hard, bleak profile as he sat beside her pretending to read the airline safety card. Just then, he turned to look at her, and their eyes met. Pawnee felt the heat rise in her cheeks. Somehow, whenever Cree expressed her unashamed admiration of Ezra, Pawnee always remembered with uncharacteristic sulkiness that he was *her* husband, after all! And then that made her angry with herself, because the marriage had been a meaningless cere- mony and Ezra was as free an agent, morally speak- ing, as she was herself, and if he and Cree liked each other, that was their own business.

''Do you think you could look a little more cheer- ful?'' he said irritably. ''You're supposed to be on your honeymoon.''

''And who told everybody so?'' she snapped back.

''You know damned well who it was. Are you sug- gesting I wanted to tell the world my business?'' Of course Miranda had tipped off the airline that they were a honeymoon couple. They were travelling first- class, and the airline knew all about how to treat a honeymoon couple in first-class. There was cham- pagne on ice for them right now.

''I thought you'd do anything that would lock me into the contract,'' said Pawnee sweetly. She couldn't understand why she kept sniping at him like this. What did she want from him? She'd made a promise and he'd held her to it, and she was resigned if any- thing, even rather excited. This was her first trip abroad, after all, and first class was a pretty good way to go, or so it seemed so far. But still she seemed to want to be getting at him all the time. For the first time in her life, Pawnee couldn't understand herself.

Ezra glared at her, irritated into responding against his will. "For a woman who thinks she has too much brain you sure don't use it much. How in the hell would my telling a few airline employees we're married lock you into anything you aren't already locked into?"

Of course he was right, but for the life of her Pawnee couldn't have said so. She just did not seem to be able to control her reactions around Ezra. The longer she knew him, the more irrational she seemed to get, and it didn't help that there was no reason for it. She sighed loudly, shrugged and turned away to look out at the bank of white cloud that covered the world from horizon to horizon.

"I hate to tear you away from such a thrilling vista," Ezra said, after a minute of wrestling with an anger that made him want to shake her. Dammit, this was an adventure, why couldn't she see that? How many women got taken to a private island for a six-month holiday? "But I'm supposed to give you this." He had opened his briefcase and now handed her a thick, glossy, blue-and-gold cardboard folder with the Polygon logo in the lower corner.

Your Introduction to Kaha Akua, she read. Opening it, she found a letter.

Dear Mrs. Jagger,
Welcome to Kaha Akua. Polygon hopes the enclosed information will be of help to you…

She glanced curiously up into Ezra's eyes. "Polygon always does an Information Pack for the project boss's wife,'' he said.

Wife. The word on his own lips made him aware of the fact that she sat on the inside with his bulk between her and the world. Made him suddenly feel that he would protect her against all comers. Ezra looked at his right hand, resting against the papers in his case. He clenched it absently, and noted with half-unconscious approval how big it was. He could look after her.

Kaha Akua, the package explained, was a privately owned island, about half the size of Maui. Always in private hands since the fall of the last Queen of Hawaii, Kaha Akua had recently been purchased by Canada's media king, Barney McNab.

Kaha Akua was in the rough shape of a figure eight lying east to west. It had two volcanic peaks of nearly equal size, one in each circle of the eight. Both volcanoes were extinct. The valley between the peaks was wild and rugged, according to the photos, which showed magnificent scenery with waterfalls and mountain pools surrounded by rain forest, leading down to beautiful white beaches surrounded by precipitous cliffs.

Just above one of these beaches was the private house of Barney McNab. Near it, also secluded, lay another much larger beach, and it was here that Polygon was building Kaha Akua's first hotel.

Not that the island did not already have visitors. On what the islanders called Sunrise, which was the smaller circle of land that lay to the east, there was a port town. It had once been a fishing port, but now was also a stop of choice of the motor and sailing yachts of the wealthy, all year-round. With its tiny population, the port had the highest per capita density of designer boutiques in the world, Pawnee learned. It was also home to several gourmet restaurants.

The western circle of the island was called Sunset. This had a coastline of precipitous green cliffs and small beaches accessible only by water. Here were the old sugar and pineapple plantations, which were slowly being converted to other types of farming to make the island more self-sufficient. There were also several cattle ranches here.

Pawnee could hardly believe her eyes. After a lifetime on a Manitoba farm it was difficult to accept, just like that, that such a place existed. Of course, she'd seen pictures like this from time to time, but never when she was en route to the place herself. There was a strange and powerful immediacy to the pictures that they'd never had before. It was as if a fairy tale she'd read as a child were suddenly coming to life.

"Is it really like this?" she asked Ezra involuntarily.

Ezra was elbow deep in his own briefing papers. But he looked up at the sound of her voice. "What?" he asked absently.

"Kaha Akua—is it really so—" she broke off.

"So what?" he prompted, frowning.

"Well, like the pictures."

He glanced down at the magical shot of a high, sparkling, crystal waterfall backed by deep green foliage, with bright flowers and an even brighter bird soaring near it. His eyes rested on it for a moment, and then lifted to her own. "We'll find out, won't we?" he grinned.

She smiled back, suddenly feeling that there was adventure ahead, and that Ezra was the perfect person to share it with.

The villa was nestled in thick rain forest on one side of a horseshoe-shaped chasm that enclosed a white beach. Lower down and closer to the beach, smaller, but no less perfect, was the guesthouse. And it was in the guesthouse that the Polygon project boss and his wife were to live for the duration of the assignment.

There were two ways into this little paradise: by sea, and by four-wheel drive over a rough track through the forest. At low tide, a third way was provided by a narrow sandbar running the length of the high wall of cliff to the adjoining beach. It was on that beach that the hotel was being built.

Ezra and Pawnee took the land route, Ezra driving the company truck assigned to him and following the one driven by his new assistant to show the way.

After two weeks of blizzard and whiteness, her skin seemed to drink the warm sunlight, and her eyes the rich green lushness. Pawnee could hardly believe she was still on the same planet. "Ezra, oh, look!" she kept saying, when a too-intensely coloured flower, or bird, or insect passed their view.

The house was wood, thatch and open spaces, designed to look like something from another century, before technology had set man apart from nature. No wall-to-wall carpet, no hum of air conditioning, but stripped wood floors covered at random with kelims woven in the designs of Pacific Coast and Polynesian tribes, and broad half-shaded balconies that were protected from the sun and let in the breeze.

The wide terrace had steps onto a narrow path that disappeared through the greenest foliage she had ever seen and reappeared a short way below, where it led onto the pure, white beach nestled between the arms of the chasm. Here the waves broke gently, and the hushing of the sea reached their ears.

It was a sound she had never heard before. Pawnee stood entranced, feeling as if she had never really breathed before.

"Ezra, listen to that sound," she breathed. "That's what they talk about, isn't it? That's the sea!"

And, like stout Cortez, she stared with eagle eyes at the Pacific, silent, upon a peak in Darien.

A note signed "Beth" informed them that she was their housekeeper and would be in later to prepare dinner for them. In the meantime, they were directed to the wet bar and the fridge, where sumptuous little snacks and rum drinks were waiting.

It is in the genes of every Canadian, the instinctive knowledge of what to do when you visit a subtropical climate in midwinter. Within half an hour Ezra and Pawnee were in shorts and thin shirts, stretched out on the inviting loungers on the terrace, drinks in their hands and the snacks within reach, watching the sun set behind the flat volcanic peak called Sunset.

"Where were you last?" Pawnee asked lazily, the conversation drifting in unimportant eddies.

"Saudi Arabia."

"I guess it's not much like this."

"It is nothing whatsoever like this," Ezra said, with as much emphasis as he could muster, feeling the sea breeze stir his hair. He raised his glass. "Who are those guys who had your sister?"

It took her a second. "Hezbuddin, you mean?"

"Here's to Hezbuddin, and all who sail in her," Ezra said solemnly. "May they never need another mosque." Then he took a hefty slug of the rum drink that had been waiting for them in the bar fridge.

Pawnee smiled. "Hezbuddin," she agreed slowly, and drank, perhaps not for quite the same reasons, but still feeling a fellow feeling with Ezra's deep satisfaction at being here.

"Hi there!" said a friendly voice behind them. They turned to meet the gaze of a small, stocky woman with straight black hair and black eyes. "Are you two ready for dinner?"

Of course Pawnee was interested to meet a citizen of Hawaii, and said so. Beth outlined her ethnic makeup for them as she served a spicy rice and sea-food dish neither Pawnee nor Ezra had ever tasted before. "I'm one-eighth Scottish, one-eighth Welsh, one-eighth Norwegian and one-eighth Chinese on my mother's side, and on my father's I'm one-quarter Hawaiian and one-eighth Irish and one-eighth Italian. So I really get around. I was raised on the Big Island, but my husband was raised right here on his parents' cattle farm, over in Sunset."

"I was raised on a farm," said Pawnee, and for a few minutes the two women discussed comparative farming techniques while Ezra tossed in the odd city-type question.

Beth didn't stay after she had served the main course, and left promising to return in the morning to discuss her schedule with Pawnee.

"Well, so much for you needing a cook-house-keeper!" Pawnee laughed when Beth had gone. "Is that one of the project boss's perks at Polygon?"

"I think she's Barney McNab's employee," said Ezra. "She looks after both places whether there's someone here or not."

Pawnee nodded absently, her mind already on other matters. "I wonder if they need any help at the farm?" she murmured, half to herself.

"What kind of help?"

"Oh, cattle droving, branding, whatever's going on at the moment. I don't know when the peak times are for a farm in this climate. I'll have to ask Beth."

Ezra looked at her quizzically. "What for?"

"Well, it's more interesting than a waiting job or a hotel job. I'm used to outdoor work, you know. I don't really like working indoors, with people."

"It's all academic anyway, isn't it?"

Pawnee forked another delicious bite of food into her mouth and chewed thoughtfully, only half her mind on the conversation. She hadn't been on a horse for a while. Boy, it would be good to be back in the saddle, working. At a couple of her jobs at country hotels she'd been able to rent a horse at nearby stables, but she hadn't enjoyed it much. The horses were mostly tired hacks, and she didn't like riding in a supervised group. To be working in the saddle, that was what she missed.

The sun set completely while they ate, and around them in the darkness the creatures of the night took over their territory. Insects sang, small animals began to forage in the underbrush and the last golden streaks in the navy sky were brushed over and obliterated.

A burst of heady perfume reached their nostrils as some flower nearby called the nocturnal insects to an assignation of the night.

Overhead, the inky sky sparkled with tiny diamond chips, and soon the moon maiden lifted herself out of the sea, and dried her glowing skin against the lush black fabric of the heavens.

The breeze that caressed their faces and stirred their hair was neither warm nor cool, but only a gentle touch. Below them, the sea rushed and murmured against the breast of the sand.

Ezra lazily reached to pour the last of the bottle of wine into their glasses, and Pawnee, gazing out at the night, lifted her hand from her glass stem. She only brushed his wrist with her fingers, that was all, but the touch was the same touch that joined the moon to the sky, the insect to the flower, the sea to the sand. All the sap of nature ran to flood this new contact with power and meaning—primitive power, primitive meaning, the surging life force that humankind had once worshipped, that nature still did.

It was as though light or electricity sparked between them, yet it was much deeper, richer, than light. It was *earth* that ran between them, not the Father, but the Mother, not spirit, but flesh. And that is a meeting with a deep, irresistible pull, like the tide of a world sea.

It was only a second—her hand continued on its journey, as did his. But now the movement of her hand as it stroked back a small lock of hair from her forehead was different—slower, lazier, as if her hand were heavy with sleep. At nature's dictate she paused, her fingers still in her hair, her elbow raised, her sleeve falling back to expose the vulnerable flesh of her inner arm, and looked at Ezra.

It was only a second's hesitation before she looked away. But Ezra's blood leapt, his flesh lifted painfully and he felt a surge of raw, animal need of her so unfamiliarly primitive it scared him. He could not look away. He saw the curve of her breast under the shirt and could feel his hand on her, as though the glass he held were her flesh.

I hope you didn't do anything to be ashamed of tonight, Ezra.

Ezra slapped the bottle down on the table like a man who'd been burnt. Jesus, had the old bastard been right all along?

It wasn't as though Ezra had never had a girlfriend. But lovemaking had always been a pretty civilised business, a pleasant building of the tension in both him and his partner...he'd never before experienced what his poor, nervous grandfather had called "the monster within, Ezra."

Not till Pawnee, with her too-thin body, her pale face and hollow eyes, her unstyled hair, her level, assessing gaze...Ezra took a hasty gulp of his wine as that gaze found his now.

"What happened?" she asked softly.

"Something bit me," he lied.

She made a little face of contrition and her eyes dropped to her glass. In Pawnee, the effects of her surroundings were slower, more melodious, less instantly recognizable, like distant music that almost summons up a memory, music that the blood hears first.

"I guess we'd better go in," he said gruffly, and she was disappointed without knowing why. "Barry's picking me up early."

Normally he would have helped her load the dishwasher, but he knew he could not withstand such proximity. He went to the bedroom instead, where he was treated to the sight of lights glowing softly from burnished wood surfaces, an invitingly turned-down bed, and his summer cotton pyjamas laid side by side with the silk-and-lace thing that had been Ben's brother's wedding gift to them.

Ezra grabbed the pyjamas and went blindly out again. The next door along the hall was a bathroom, and next to that another bedroom. There were no sheets on the bed, but he didn't need sheets. He undressed and lay on the mattress under the woven cotton spread and tried not to wonder whether Pawnee was putting on the silk thing, and what she would do if his need drove him to her bed in the night.

8

There is nothing that can compare to that first morning of waking up to pineapple and frangipani blossom, the sun slanting warm, and birdsong on the breeze through an open window. Ezra and Pawnee awoke in their separate rooms to the same summons from an unknown bird, the same distant sound of the surf inviting them up.

They met in the bathroom. Ezra had time to notice, before he clumsily bowed out, that she was wearing a long, pale green T-shirt, and not the lacy item that no doubt Miranda had been responsible for packing.

Pawnee noticed that, just like in a book, Ezra slept in his bottoms but not his tops, and that his chest looked at lot more imposing naked than clothed. He didn't have hair on his chest, but he had a lot of what looked like hard muscle. And a slim waist and hips. And with his deep brown, glossy hair tousled from sleep and his face unshaven, he looked altogether less gentle and more giant.

She was quick in the bathroom, brushing her teeth and washing her face were all the ablutions she performed: she wasn't going to shower when there was all that ocean out there. She knocked on Ezra's door before she left, calling, "Bathroom's free!" It was nothing more than she was used to doing at Sam's place, but somehow everything seemed different here, more intimate. She went back into the bedroom and rooted out her old serviceable black swimsuit and slid her legs into it.

Five minutes later she emerged onto the balcony to see that Ezra had had the same thought. He was wearing a snug pair of speed-swimming trunks and had a towel around his neck. With a word of greeting, they went down the steps and followed the path down to the sea, all the devotion of religious initiates in their hearts: this was the Great Mystery. This was why Canadians ritually performed the journey south for two weeks in winter.

The two jutting arms of the cliffs formed a breakwater for this little inset beach, giving them their own private, almost serene bay, bright blue now against the white of the sand. Out beyond those arms the sea broke much more forcefully against the black volcanic rock.

Pawnee had never seen the sea before, but she was a good strong swimmer, and she loved water. She dived excitedly into a swell, laughing as it broke over her head, and came up spluttering, her eyes stinging, a strange taste in her mouth.

"What is it?" she demanded, her fingers pressing her eyes. "What's that funny taste?"

Ezra, drenched by the same wave, drops of water glistening on his hair and lashes, laughed aloud. "Salt!" he said. "You'll get used to it."

"Salt! Of course! How wonderful!" Pawnee sang. "Do you know I've never been in salt water before?"

Ezra fell backwards into the next surging wave and kicked off. "Well, come on in!" he said, and then rolled over; and his long, strong arms began a rhythmic stroke that drew him swiftly away from her. Pawnee gave herself up to the water's silken embrace and followed him.

They had coffee and fresh pineapple for breakfast, sitting on the terrace again, talking about nothing, and something, and then nothing again. Ezra had never felt so easy with a woman before. When they weren't fighting, he just felt comfortable with Pawnee. He couldn't remember what they talked about five minutes after the conversation was over, but that was the point: it just happened. He thought back to those dates Miranda had set up for him, and to many similar experiences in the past. He could generally remember those conversations—if you could call them that—because he had been so uncomfortably aware that he didn't know what to say or how to say it.

He had problems with Pawnee, but nerves wasn't one of them.

When Barry showed up, he'd forgotten to dress, and had to hurry off to change, leaving his new assistant with Pawnee on the terrace, Barry saying, "Maybe your wife will give me a cup of coffee," and Pawnee smiling, "Sure. Just let me get you a cup."

Your wife. He liked the thought of Pawnee playing hostess for him. It was like being a team.

"You married?" he asked Barry later, as they made the quick journey by truck down to the site.

"No, but Gord is," Barry said. Ezra recognized the

name of his new assistant. "Sonia was pretty sorry when Gerry and his wife Susan had to leave, so I don't think it'll be long before she's out here to meet Pawnee."

"Good," Ezra said comfortably. "Pawnee'll get pretty bored on her own all the time."

"Believe me, she won't get bored with Sonia around. Sonia's got this island sewed up, according to Gord. He's always saying she's like a divining rod—take her to a trackless waste and within an hour Sonia would find somewhere to shop."

But Pawnee was already taking care of things in her own way. By ten o'clock, having worked out a schedule with Beth that suited them both, she was pitching for a job on Beth's husband's farm.

"I run the house, and leave the farm to Bert," Beth said. "He does hire now and then, but I don't know if he's looking now. Why don't you come over and talk to him one of these days?"

"Maybe I could go back with you now," Pawnee suggested, and shortly afterwards she was driving the truck across the ranch and feeling more at home than she'd felt for two long years.

When she described her history and qualifications to Bert, he was impressed, and when he took her out on horseback to look over the ranch, he saw how at home she was in the saddle and knew she hadn't lied.

"If you're willing to pitch in and do whatever's needed," said Bert hesitantly, because he'd never hired a female hand before. Pawnee assured him again that she could turn her hand to whatever was going. "Well, all right, then. You're Canadian, right?"

Pawnee nodded.

"I guess I'd better have a look at your H2 certificate, there'll probably be some form I have to fill out.''

"My H2 certificate?"

"If that's what you've got. Have you got something else? It's a work visa for nonspecialist occupations.''

"Oh, right! Well, I'm sure there'll be no problem about that. I'll talk to my husband, I'm sure the company must have made some arrangement for me.''

She drove back to the house on the bay in high good humour, well pleased with herself and the prospect of literally getting into the saddle again. She realized now that she had been too demanding before. Her agriculture degree had made her feel she ought to be running a farm. But she would have been better off hiring out as a hand over the past two years rather than doing the kind of work she'd been doing in hotels and restaurants.

There wouldn't be much time for sunbathing now—she expected long hours on the ranch—so when she arrived at the house Pawnee put on her swimsuit, grabbed up a towel and some suntan lotion and went down to the water.

Ezra found her there an hour later, playing in the waves like a dolphin. He got into his own trunks and went down to join her.

"Hi!" she called, well pleased to have some company. "Are you home for lunch, or is your day over?"

"Lunch," he said. "Just thought I'd check to see how you're getting on." *I guess you'll be going home to your wife,* Barry had said, showing him the crew mess, and suddenly that had seemed like a very good thing to do.

Pawnee dragged her hair out of her eyes as she came up from a dive to the bottom. "I've lost my hair elastic," she said absently. "I suppose it's out at sea already."

"Where'd you learn to swim?" Ezra asked a few minutes later, as they moved through the lush green foliage up to the balcony. It seemed odd that he did not know this fact about his wife. Half the time he felt as if he'd always known her.

"In the school pool," she said. "I used to compete for my high school, but then there was just too much to do on the farm, so I gave that up. But at agricultural college, when there was nothing to do, I took it up again. Swimming, not competing." After so long working so hard, the relative ease of university life had felt like unemployment to Pawnee, even with the part-time job she'd got to help pay her way. She'd wandered like a lost soul till she learned the university had a pool. "This is sure different, isn't it? Where did you learn?"

"Pretty much the same. I competed for my varsity team, but size slows you down. I never won anything individual."

They were in the house by this time, Pawnee poking around to see what might do for lunch, Ezra laying the table on the balcony.

"Did you know there's a pool up at the other house?" Pawnee called out to him. "Beth told me today we're free to use it as long as no one's in residence up there. It's okay when he and his wife are there, but if they've lent it to somebody else—you know, some business associate or celebrity—we're asked not to use it.''

"Have you been up there to check it out?"

"Not yet." She joined him on the terrace with a laden tray, and Ezra immediately jumped to take it from her. "Thanks." She pulled the trolley forward for him to set the tray on. Both of them took subliminal pleasure in the easy way they worked together. "Beth says it's really, really fabulous. Maybe we should try it out tonight."

Lunch was salad, cold meat, quiche and fresh bread and butter, and a tray of fruit piled high. And a truly great cup of coffee. Ezra thought of all the lunches he had eaten in fly-bitten crew messes in fly-ridden deserts—lousy ersatz coffee, flavourless, chemical-soaked meats and vegetables imported in packages, tins, freezer packs, and cooked by uninspired company cooks...he looked at Pawnee and thought that so far he hadn't discovered one drawback to being married to her.

"Gord told me this morning that his wife wants to meet you. She's planning on coming around this afternoon." Ezra grinned. "Apparently Sonia can introduce you to all the best places to shop."

Pawnee smiled. Of course it would be nice to meet a potential friend, but she had better things to do than shop. "Okay."

Ezra cleared his throat. "Ah—I just want—well, you can feel pretty free in the shops, you know. I'm making good money here, real good money, and I haven't got anything to spend it on—well, I'd like you to feel free to buy some nice things."

He really meant it. He'd dragged her here against

her will, the least he could do was give her a wardrobe to take home. He'd noticed her clothes all seemed plain, and well-worn. He supposed the family farm had been suffering for quite awhile before it went under. So she'd probably like the chance to do some real shopping. Also, he liked the idea of being able to buy clothes for his wife.

He remembered the short little dress she'd been wearing at the restaurant on their wedding night and hoped she'd buy something sexy like that. He tried hard not to think of the little silky thing they'd got for a wedding present from Luke and Carol. He really tried hard not to hope she'd buy things like that, and maybe want to wear them for him someday…

Pawnee nodded. "Thanks. I'll need some good serviceable jeans and shirts, that's for sure."

Ezra came down with a bump. *"Jeans?"*

"Yeah, you'll never guess what I've been doing this morning—I've got myself a job already!" She grinned at him, inviting him to share her pleasure. "On Bert and Beth's ranch! Isn't that great? I start Monday."

"A job? A job doing what?"

"Just—whatever there is, you know. A bit of fence repair, and branding, and riding out…there's always something to do. Bert doesn't just have cattle, he's got a small home farm, too, just like Mom and Dad did. So I've got just the right experience."

Ezra was looking at her with his mouth half-open, and she frowned irritably. What on earth was his problem? Surely he hadn't imagined she was going to sit around all day painting her nails?

"What's the matter?" she demanded.

"You didn't read your familiarization kit," he said softly.

"Yes, I did, most of it."

"You missed the page that tells you your husband is on an H1 visa. That automatically makes you H4."

Pawnee frowned. She certainly didn't recall reading anything like that. "What does that mean?"

"It means that as spouse of the H1-holder you're not entitled to take work here."

"What are you talking about? This is the States, not Shamsirabia! We've got a free-trade agreement!"

"This is a foreign country, Pawnee," he said doggedly, "and you are not allowed to work here. And if you try anything stupid like working illegally, I'll be out of a job as soon as Barney McNab hears of it, which will be after about three minutes. This is a small place."

"Bert didn't think there'd be any trouble! He said all I needed was an H2 certificate and it would be okay!" she exclaimed. "Don't you think he knows the laws of his own country?"

"I'm sure he does," Ezra said patiently. "If you want an H2 certificate, you have to apply before you enter the country. You can go to Oahu and apply for one, Pawnee, because you've got a pretty good excuse for not getting prior approval, with the wedding happening in such a hurry. But it will probably take months to be processed, and you probably won't get one in the end. An H2 certificate is for temporary nonspecialist labour, and they don't like to give them out."

Pawnee had slowly put down her fork during this little speech, and her eyes were going wider and wider with horror as she stared at him. "Are you telling me *I can't work at all?*" she almost screeched.

He nodded. "It's the way it's always been. Polygon is very damn strict about it, and rumour says McNab's even worse."

"But Americans work in Canada all the time! I was *always* working with Americans and Australians doing casual labour at the hotels I worked in."

He only shrugged. There was nothing he could do about that, and Pawnee knew it. She was just letting off steam, so he let her do it.

"What about waiting in a café or something, just part-time?" she demanded desperately. "Can I do that?"

"You can't work in this country," he said evenly.

"But what am I going to *do,* for God's sake?" Pawnee's brain was reeling with shock. She had always worked, all her life! Hard work had been her life from as early as she could remember, from the time when she had toddled after her father on his chores, and he had always given her something useful to do. She had measured her growth against the legs of horses, which she had curried from the time she could only reach as far as the knee. She had measured her increasing strength against the amount of feed she could carry in a bucket. She had never taken a real holiday since the age of twelve, when interest rates on her father's modernization loan had skyrocketed. In college, her holidays had all been spent at home on the farm, trying desperately to find a way to save it…and when everything had failed, when they had had to face it and give up, when the bank representative had walked in and said those terrible, sickening words to her father…Pawnee had gone out and got a job. It hadn't been difficult for someone who was willing and used to hard work and long hours.

Except for the four weeks while Cree was hostage, Pawnee had never been out of work in her life.

"Ezra, what will I *do?*" she repeated, in a horrified whisper when she had confided some of this to him.

He felt suddenly protective of her, felt with irrational masculinity that it wasn't right that such a slim, small woman should have had to work so miserably hard all her life that she didn't even know how to cope with the thought of idleness! Felt with stupid hubris that if only he'd been there, she'd have been better looked after.

"If you figure it at two weeks annual vacation ever since the age of twelve, that's about six months," he told her. "It's simple. What you're going to do is take all the back holiday you're owed in one go. And face it, Pawnee, you couldn't ask for a better place than Hawaii to take it in."

"Oh, don't worry, there's lots to do!" Sonia assured her later that afternoon. "My gosh, I've learned to scuba and I've really improved my tennis…there's lots going on here because of the yachts, you see. Can you play tennis?"

Tennis? Tennis was for the idle rich. "No," said Pawnee flatly.

"Well, John is a terrific coach, and I'm sure he can fit you in somewhere. Oh, and…" Sonia flicked an eye over Pawnee's hair. It was clear that it had last been cut with nail scissors in a mirror, but she pretended not to notice. "…you'll just love what Caroline can do to hair! She's very, very expensive, she's Paris-trained and can charge the earth here, and she does! But you'll love her. I'm actually due for a trim tomorrow,'' she lied brightly. ''Why don't I phone for an appointment for you, too?''

To this at least Pawnee could agree. Her hair was just at that length where an elastic wouldn't hold it properly, and it was certainly getting in the way when she swam.

''If she'll just hack this off short, I'll be happy,'' she said.

Sonia only smiled. She would prime Caroline on the phone before they went in. That hair certainly needed a conditioning treatment as well as a good cut.

''And while we're at it, why don't we do the whole number? I'll book us for a massage and skin treatment at Frankie's salon.''

Pawnee sighed. ''I guess so,'' she said unhappily.

If she had known that Sonia was planning her complete makeover and transformation, she'd have been a lot more unhappy. But fortunately Sonia had the sense to keep her project to herself. Well, at least she kept it from *Pawnee*. By nightfall, half the boutique owners in Port Sunrise were party to the conspiracy.

9

The pool at the big house was a marvel of technology assisting nature with no thought for cost. Behind the house there was a small waterfall. Under this waterfall engineering had created a "natural" rock pool on two levels, capturing the water, diverting it briefly from its course and gently channelling it to make a forest paradise before allowing it to escape again and continue its journey to the sea.

The pool was away from the house, set amongst trees against the cliff face. Swimming in it, relaxing beside it, you looked straight out to the ocean and could imagine yourself alone in Eden. The water was crystal clear and cold, and Pawnee and Ezra soon discovered that there was no better way to start the day than to swim there.

Pawnee, in fact, seemed to be spending most of her time in the water, and she was amazed how many different things "water" could be. Nearly every day she had a scuba diving lesson near Port Sunrise, and then the water was half friend, half enemy, whom she must learn to respect and be wary of, and who would not reveal its mysteries and magic until she was an adept.

She also snorkelled at a shallow coral reef close to the diving school, as a kind of promise of what was to come when she had learned to dive. Then the water was another world, where she could forget time existed, where she could almost become another species.

She often returned to swim again from the beach in the late afternoon, and then again with Ezra when he got home from the site. At these times, with the late sun turning the water golden, the ocean's silken caress was yet another sort of pleasure. Then she felt part, not of the undersea life, but of the water itself, part of the being named *ocean*.

After sunset it was unwise to swim in the sea. Sometimes they finished the day as they had begun it, walking up to the pool in the darkness and swimming with the stars as their only light.

Often in the stillness they talked, for minutes or hours, just sitting in the magic of the night, watching the sky, listening to the rush and burble of the waterfall. It was here that Ezra found himself talking about things he had never told anyone. About the death of his parents, about how much he had hated the move to Toronto, how cold his grandparents had seemed after family life out west.

He talked about other things, too—things that fascinated her. Countries he'd visited and worked in, how strange their customs sometimes seemed. And he listened—to the story of her upbringing, of her love for the land, of the heartbreaking loss of it.

Of course there was lots that he never told Pawnee, much that he couldn't put into words, or that he scarcely remembered. But there were long periods that they spent without speaking, too, around the forest pool, and it sometimes seemed to Ezra that his silence in that place told her as much about him as words could.

Pawnee was amazed at how full your day could be when you were doing nothing productive. When she wasn't in the water, she shopped and ate lunch with Sonia. She started tennis lessons on a couple of afternoons a week. She was often invited aboard the yachts for drinks by people hungry for a new face, eager to gossip about Barney McNab and his new island and his hotel.

It wasn't just the yachties who gossiped about the new hotel. It only took a few days for Pawnee to become uncomfortably aware of how much hostility there was to the project. She could even understand it. The hotel was going to be far too big for the island—a central hotel smack on the beach and a whole lot of outbuildings, and a giant swimming pool. It had always been a favourite beach for the locals, those with little boats, anyway, who had traditionally always gone to that beach when they wanted to get away from the larger, much more accessible beach near Port Sunrise. Now it would be completely spoiled by concrete and glass and a thousand tourists. Trees were being uprooted by the dozens. Wildlife was being disturbed and habitats destroyed.

Pawnee heard all about it. People often did not realize she was connected with the site. They thought she was from one of the yachts. And they complained freely to her, hating Barney McNab, hating the men who did his bidding, hating their ruined future.

Pawnee didn't say anything to Ezra about it, because what could he do? He had taken over a job already begun; he'd said to her some time ago that all the concrete was already poured…it would do no good to take a stand, because Polygon would simply replace him.

She wished things were otherwise. She thought of Miranda's confidence in Barney McNab's environmental integrity and wished with all her heart that it had been so. But she supposed rich men were rich men the world over, and always would be.

Ezra drove slowly, forcing his unwilling concentration, knowing he should have let Barry drive him after all. Thank God it was a short drive, and he wasn't likely to meet anyone else on it, because he could see his reactions were slow.

He was worried. Accidents did happen on building sites, but two injuries to two successive project bosses might be more than coincidence. He knew there was a certain amount of hostility among the residents; they thought the hotel project was the beginning of the end of the quiet life. It was all right for Port Sunrise to be there; it had been going for decades and didn't impinge on the rest of the island much. But the hotel somehow frightened them. They were sure the next thing would be something two miles high in concrete and glass.

He knew some of the local men who had taken jobs on the site were being ostracized; was one of them trying to prove his island solidarity by sabotage? Or was it possible they'd hired a saboteur in the first place?

Or maybe it was just what it seemed: an accident.
A block coming loose and falling on him, hitting less
hard than it might have because he'd seen its shadow
and managed to dodge. It had hit his head, but glanc-
ingly; his shoulder had taken more of a blow, but
even it was not broken. Thank God. The doctor had
done what little he could and then ordered Ezra home
till they could be sure he didn't have a concussion.

He hoped Pawnee would be there. Over the past
couple of weeks, according to what she told him of
her daily activities, she'd hardly been home. He
wasn't sure what she did: scuba, she was very excited
about that, and she'd got herself some clothes and a
new swimsuit. And she'd been exploring the island.
But that was all he knew for sure.

If she was out he'd just pour himself something
long and cold and stretch out on the terrace. But he'd
rather she was there.

The truck that McNab provided with the house was
parked at an efficient angle just off the track, but it
wasn't proof she was in. He knew Sonia sometimes
picked Pawnee up in her own vehicle. Ezra pulled the
company truck up beside it at not nearly so neat an
angle, and stumbled out. His shoulder was pretty
painful now, and his head ached. He walked into the
cool of the house and then out onto the terrace. There
was an empty glass beside one of the loungers, but
no one was in it.

"Ezra!"

Pawnee had been in the kitchen and hadn't heard
him arrive. She stood rooted with surprise as he
turned to her, and blushed self-consciously when his
eyes narrowed as he took her in.

Two weeks and Sonia's determination had made big changes in Pawnee's appearance. He'd noted them, bit by bit, but now he got the full benefit of the transformation all at once.

Her embarrassment was lost in the greater emotion when she noticed the bandage on his head. "Ezra? What's happened? Are you hurt?" she said in concern.

She'd cut her hair short, and it was now a glossy dark cap curling round her well-shaped little head, emphasising the proud ancestral bloodline of the cheekbones and jaw. And she'd gained weight, putting just enough flesh on to cover the model's thinness with smooth, gentle curves, without disguising the long, firm muscle underneath. She was tanned a pleasant nutty shade that also emphasised that tribal blood she was so proud of, and he could smell from here that what gave her skin that creamy, well-oiled look was coconut oil.

And she was all but naked. It took him a moment to see that she wasn't completely naked, the way he'd thought at first: She was wearing a bikini bottom straight out of the jungle, in what looked like fawn-coloured chamois leather, cut high at the thigh and rolled and braided just below the waist as if she were Jane. But except for a coral bracelet she *was* otherwise naked, and his masculine brain—if it could be called that—noted with deep, responsive approval the high, firm roundness of her naked breasts, the way the nipples tightened as he looked at them, as if she felt his glance as a physical touch.

He certainly did. He squeezed his hands into fists because just looking at her, apparently, he could feel her creamy skin against his palms. *His wife's skin,* part of his brain whispered, as it had been whispering more and more often lately.

Damn, damn, damn. His blood pounded in his temples, and he felt the powerful stirring of it, not just in his loins, but through his whole being. He was turning into an animal where he stood, someone who couldn't keep his hands off his own wife...but of course, most men weren't trying to keep their hands off their wives...

"Dammit!" he exploded. "Can't you put something on?"

Her shock and surprise had made her forget herself, but at his words she blushed and rushed to the lounger, snatching up her shirt and buttoning it on before turning to face him again.

It wasn't much better, from Ezra's point of view. It was a little jungle shirt that matched the little jungle bottoms, two buttons down the front, with a tiny upstanding collar, sleeveless and falling barely to her midriff. The sleeve edges and the bottom edge were all roughly jagged. All that was missing was a dagger at her belt.

"Me Tarzan," he said stupidly, and he damned well felt like Tarzan.

"You're hurt," she said. "Come and sit down."

She adjusted the overhead awning to shade the balcony, and he sank gratefully into a lounger and put his feet up. "Would you like some piña colada juice?" she asked, and when he nodded, disappeared. She came back with a tray and set it down on the little table beside him. A pitcher of the creamy white juice and a platter of freshly cut fruit.

As she bent down to serve him, he couldn't help noticing the long, smooth curves of her legs, her bare arms and the way her waist curved into her hips…he began to think he might have been better off if she had taken that job on the ranch, and wore jeans and serviceable shirts around the place.

The lounger was wide; as she handed him a glass she sank down beside his hips and looked at him with concern. "What happened?"

"A piece of concrete," he said lightly. He hadn't thought about her being worried like this. He'd never had a woman concerned about his well-being before, not on a job. Sam had always been there when he went home, of course, she was always interested, but this was different.

Pawnee sucked in her breath. "Ezra!" she whispered. "Was it—?" she broke off.

"We're calling it an accident," he said calmly. "It may have been one."

"Should you be in bed?"

Ezra shut his eyes and wrestled with the animal within.

She mistook the grimace for one of pain, and the next thing he felt was her hand against the skin of his forehead, then his cheek. "Can I get you something?" she asked softly. "Have you had any pain-killers?"

He opened his eyes, and his look burned right into her at close quarters, and whether it was the combination of sun and sea and sheer physical well-being, or whether it was just Ezra's sheer animal maleness at point-blank range, Pawnee felt that look right to the roots of her being. The smell of her coconut oil was suddenly strongly seductive, and her thighs slithered against each other, and his cheek was both rough and smooth against her hand.

He took her wrist in his grasp, holding it there as, without conscious volition, he turned his face and buried his mouth against her supersensitive palm. Her indrawn breath was audible, and he felt the responsive surge in his system.

Against the side of his lips he felt the cool metal of a ring. He paused. The ring he had put there. Her wedding ring. He turned his mouth and convulsively pressed his lips over the ring, sucking at her finger, trying to draw it between his lips. His ring, the ring he had put there. The ring that meant…

Pawnee sat frozen in astonishment at the way the kiss of his lips washed through her, over her, bathing her whole body in heat. She watched as his eyes closed with desire and felt how his grip on her tightened mercilessly as he forced her hand against his hungry mouth.

When he looked up, her own eyes were half shut with the strength of her physical and mental response, and when he saw that, Ezra was gone. His other hand came up to enclose her upper arm, and he pulled her irresistibly down against him, as both his hands crept up to her head and drew her face in for his hungry kiss.

She did not resist. She was beyond resisting, beyond even knowing that resistance was a choice. When his mouth found hers, she moaned with the sheer, unexpected assault of pleasure on her system.

The sound went to his brain like wildfire. It scorched him, making his body leap painfully, his hands press her...her breast was against his palm now, his hand had slipped under the little top, searching for the fullness he wanted, and finding it.

Roughly he shoved the top out of his way and, lifting her, bending his head, brought the nipple within reach of his mouth.

The heat of his mouth enclosed her, and his arm was like steel against her back. She was helpless, her strength was nothing against his, and the knowledge that this was so fuelled her body's wild pleasure in the touch. She cried out again, and again.

He had never wanted a woman like this in his life. He felt as though he was nothing but his own sex. Her cries were the most sensual, sexual thing he'd ever experienced. He felt a wave building in him, a wave stronger than any he had ever felt, a wave of passion and desire that seemed deeper than his own soul, that threatened to swamp reason completely.

I hope you weren't too much of an animal tonight, Ezra. Beware the animal within.

Suddenly she was sitting on the edge of the lounger again, and he was holding her away, and not against him.

"Ezra?" she whispered.

He was swearing under his breath, his eyes shut. "Sorry, Pawnee," he said. "Damn, I'm sorry. It's not part of the deal, is it?"

The gentle breeze that blew over the terrace suddenly felt cold. Pawnee shivered. "No, it's not part of the deal," she agreed tonelessly.

"I'm sorry. Did I scare you?"

Scare her? "No, you didn't scare me." She rubbed her eyes with one hand, feeling the thwarted desire in her body turn against her, making her sick and shaky. She stood up. She wasn't sure how much she had given away of her feelings, but she was sure Ezra was experienced enough to know that she had wanted him pretty fiercely. She felt deeply humiliated, not understanding why he had begun, why he had stopped.

"Don't ever do that again, Ezra," she said flatly, not sure herself what she meant, only knowing that she could not bear such a humiliation often.

"No," he agreed. He wanted to curse, to throw the entire contents of the balcony into the sea. What had he just done? What the hell had he done?

In the morning, his shoulder ached and was black and blue, but there was nothing wrong with his head beyond a bit of soreness around the abrasion. He could use the shoulder as an excuse not to go up to the pool, and he could use the fact of having left the site early yesterday as an excuse to get in early this morning. He drank a cup of coffee in embarrassed silence while Pawnee mostly pottered in the kitchen, and then was gone.

Pawnee took her towel and snorkel and went straight up to the little paradise. Somehow, today, floating in the blissfully pure water, she was aware that one day it would be only a memory, and that she would never come back. She knew that what she would miss most of all was this pool, the moments she had had here with Ezra, when the magic had seemed to promise her a different future...

But it had been all unconscious. Until this moment, she hadn't understood what she was dreaming—hadn't understood *that* she was dreaming. Until now she had honestly had no idea that she was falling in love with Ezra.

She had lain awake for much of the night, tossing and thinking, reeling from the pain of the first sexual rejection she'd ever experienced...it was only here and now, in the paradise from which it was inevitable she would be expelled, that she understood.

Half of paradise was the beautiful surroundings. The other half was being in it with Ezra. And it was that half that it was going to kill her to lose.

Pawnee's trouble—and probably Ezra knew it, she told herself—was that she had zero sexual experience. For this two circumstances were largely responsible: her father and the recession.

Every boy she had dated at the age of fifteen and sixteen had been scared to death of her father. He had had a way of looking at boys that told them they'd be dealing with him if they messed around with his daughter. For two years, while everybody around them seemed to be experimenting with the great secret, Pawnee—and Cree—had been chastely delivered home by a boy determined to be able to look Jack Walker in the eye—and knowing he would have to.

Then recession had hit the country, and her father, who had been fighting to keep the farm afloat ever since his farm loan had been hit by soaring interest rates in the early eighties, was struggling more and more desperately to survive. Pawnee's social life had all but disappeared as she worked side by side with him.

Later, at her father's insistence, she had unwillingly gone to agricultural college. She knew now that he had already looked the future in the eye, and that he was determined that she should have something to carry on with when the farm was gone. Maybe he had even hoped that she would meet a farmer's son and get married. But to her he had talked about needing the modern techniques that she would learn about to save the farm.

By then she was nineteen years old and hadn't dated for over two years. She felt like a backward child—as though all the rest of the world knew some secret that she had failed to learn. And she knew nothing about films, about music, scarcely anything about politics…this awkwardness kept her from accepting dates, fearing that she would somehow be exposed as a fool.

She had discovered the university swimming pool, and although she was consciously unaware of the mechanism at work, had put all her considerable sexual energy into that outlet. Life became easier after that. When she felt jumpy with an unrecognized tension, Pawnee went for a swim.

But swimming wasn't an outlet for sexual energy when you were swimming with the man who was the source of your sexual tension in the first place. Pawnee had watched Ezra, day by day, a healthy man at peak sexual maturity, his skin glistening, his muscles rippling, his wet lashes curved and sparkling with pleasure, and her hormones had clamoured louder and louder…until yesterday the message had deafened her.

Pawnee put on a mask, rolled over in the water and dived deep down into the silky, mysterious green depths. Most of the higher pool was a natural crevice in the rocks that had only needed enlarging by shoring it up at one edge. Against the cliff face a thousand little fishes nibbled at the green growth.

She realized with a curious sense of longing that these fish had never left the Garden of Eden. Such creatures of the wild were still living like her own hunter-gatherer ancestors, in a world so rich you only put out your hand and ripe fruit fell into it.

Only humankind had left the protection of the divine cloak and embarked on the long, tortuous, troubled journey to knowledge and consciousness, naked and afraid…

She was naked and afraid. While she had not realized she loved Ezra, she had been like these fishes, nibbling bits of happiness, feeding at the rock of security without real awareness of her state.

Paradise, she realized, is when you are given what you need without knowing *that* you need.

Now she knew that she needed Ezra, that she wanted him with a physical hunger and a mental necessity whose seeds had probably been driving her since that first meeting with him.

Now she had been cast out of Eden.

Because it was very clear that, although Ezra might be experiencing sexual need himself, he did not see Pawnee as the woman to fulfil his need.

10

━━➤ ◀━━

That morning Ezra was like a bear with a sore head, and it wasn't just because he had a sore head. He was sore at himself, sore at life, sore at Pawnee.

Himself mostly. What the hell had possessed him? She'd been kissing him, *wanting* him, he was sure of it, and why had that terrified him? Just thinking of it now made the animal stir in him. He could feel its unfamiliar wildness, its frustration, like a caged panther lashing its tail. He'd never been bothered by such ferocity before. Why now? What the hell was it about one tough-minded little woman, supple, shining, getting more and more luscious by the day...

"Ezra, dammit, you in there or what?"

"What?"

"I'm trying to talk to you!"

"Sorry, sorry! Tell me again."

Gord looked at him with a sudden thought. "You sure that doctor did all the tests he should have yesterday?"

Ezra cursed mentally. That was all he needed—a rumour that he'd been brain damaged. "Yeah, I'm fine, I was just thinking about something else."

Damn, damn, damn.

* * *

Very low tide revealed a sandbar strip running around one side of the bay and along in front of the cliff face and the ocean. Pawnee knew it led to the next bay, where the hotel development was being built, but she had never walked there, partly because the sandbar was above the waterline for such a short time, partly because she didn't really want to see the depredations that were taking place. Late that afternoon, as she sat on the beach in a loose cotton dress, the tide went out, and the sandbar was suddenly revealed like a pink path through the water, leading to Ezra. She found the invitation too compelling. Not letting herself think of consequences, she stood up and set off.

The tide was already on the turn. She would not be able to return the way she had come, said a warning in her head. But she was being drawn as surely as a sailor by a siren of the sea. She had no time to think of coming back. All her focus was on getting there. She needed to see Ezra, like thirst in the desert.

Don't ever do that again, Ezra, she'd said. Ezra shook his head irritably. Don't do what? Don't try to make love to her? Or don't stop in the middle?

He was damn sure he wouldn't stop in the middle again, once he got started. The old man's poison had stopped working as of now. Ezra was good and mad at himself, but something had happened—he wasn't afraid of himself anymore. He wasn't afraid because, having met his animal head-on at last, after years of running from it, he understood one thing—his animal had no other goal than pleasure, for Pawnee as well as for himself.

He supposed his grandfather, the poor bastard, had never understood that women enjoyed sex. Maybe he'd learned to consider his desires, his quest for pleasure, as an evil because of that. But Ezra had taken a very different message from his warnings. He had unconsciously come to fear that "the animal within" must by nature be vicious if given its head. There were plenty of men proving that thesis in the world, and at seventeen he guessed the possibility had horrified him.

Women had complained to him in the past that he was too "controlled." He had never understood what they were complaining about. He'd had no idea that what they had wanted was for him to lose his head. He'd thought, even if only unconsciously, that any sane woman hoped and prayed that a lover would keep his head.

Well, he wouldn't be controlled around Pawnee. He wasn't capable of it, and now he knew it wasn't necessary. It had taken his response to Pawnee to show him the truth. And she might be nervous, but she was not afraid of him. There was no reason why she should be.

He would give her only pleasure. He would make her faint with pleasure, and then he supposed he would faint himself, because that little whisper of excitement from her yesterday had about blown the top of his head off...

The only problem was, how to convince her he wouldn't push her away again. How to get her to give in again as openly as she'd been ready to do yesterday.

The problem was, how to seduce his wife.

* * *

Pawnee rounded the edge of the cliff and stared in astonishment at the little village above her in the forest. A dozen little half-built South Sea shanties were sprinkled among the trees, as if a two-hundred-year-old fishing village were springing into existence all at once. Lower down, tucked in against a corner formed by the cliffs, a larger octagonal shape was also apparently sprouting. A high waterfall thundered from the wall of cliff and ran down through a swirl of pools overhung with rich green foliage.

Men in hard hats were coming and going all over the site. Nearer to the water's edge were the temporary structures of three yellow construction huts, and a crane. A sign on the door of one of them informed her that it was the office.

She'd felt drawn here, but now that she was here, she didn't know what to do. Nervousness woke her a little from her trance of need. Ezra had never suggested that she should visit him at the site, and after yesterday, what would her sudden appearance make him think? Would he imagine she was desperate for his attentions? Why on earth had she come?

She turned on the thought, but she was too late. Already the waves were rushing over the little path of sand. The way home was gone.

"Is that a mermaid? Where the heck did she spring from?"

They were standing on the edge of one of the pools, while Ezra and George and Gord discussed a problem that had belatedly appeared with the waterfall and pool. The men had downed tools and were just leaving.

Gord, McNab's architect on several projects around the world, fascinated by what had been done with the natural waterfall behind the house, had suggested constructing one here from scratch. It was a closed system he'd designed himself—pools, filtration system, waterfall—and it was in the cards, Ezra knew, that there would be wrinkles to be ironed out. In fact, this was the one thing most likely to take them over budget.

At George's words, Ezra suddenly recognized the prickle in his neck hairs for what it was, and whirling, almost fell into the pool.

Gord said, "It's Pawnee," but he spoke to the air, because Ezra was already on his way down to the beach.

He saw her turn and splash back towards the cliff, then hesitate, her back to him. "Pawnee!" he called. He was practically running flat out by this time, but he didn't really notice the fact, nor that almost every man still on the site had turned at the sound of his shout and stopped to watch his rapid progress across the beach.

He was aware that she had stopped, and was waiting for him with wary eyes. "Hi!" he said, coming up to her. They stood looking at each other while Ezra panted.

"Hi," she said. He was wearing a hard hat, short-sleeve shirt, khaki shorts and work boots. She could see drops of sweat glistening amongst the tiny curling hairs on his bare thighs. "I guess I'm interrupting your work."

He shook his head. "Come and see the place," he offered. He had just enough self-control not to grab her in front of everybody. He took her arm and turned her around, and then put his arm around her back, unconsciously possessive, guiding her up the beach. And there wasn't a man on the site who didn't instantly recognize that the boss had one hell of a cute little wife, and that he'd about break the legs of any man stupid enough to try to tell her so.

Ezra felt her withdraw from his touch. Nothing you could see from the outside, but he knew the difference between a woman who melted into the protection of a man and one who kept herself independent. Right. So it wasn't going to be easy. There weren't going to be quick solutions. He'd have to take it slowly and carefully.

Well, he could do that. He could take his time. He had a whole lifetime, if he played it right.

Pawnee was wishing he wouldn't touch her like that, with such impersonal protectiveness. It made her want to sink in against him and pull the world after, and once she started doing something like that, who knew where she'd end? Begging him, probably. Weeping that she loved him…what a mess that would be.

His possessively curving hand rested gently against her, now her waist, now her hip, as they walked up the beach to the building marked Office. "You're barefoot," he observed, and she agreed. There would be no loose nails in the office, but up on the actual site he would be careful where he took her.

She had met a number of the men during the past weeks, Gord and Barry and a few others had dropped around for drinks, and they had run into others in Port Sunrise from time to time. Ezra introduced her to one or two she hadn't met as he and Gord guided her around the site in the rays of the setting sun.

Never had men been so politely respectful. She'd had no idea that building construction workers could be unchauvinistic. At home they tended to whistle and call at her, but here it was as if they were talking to a nun.

Or, of course, an attractive, sexy woman under the protection of a very big, very dangerous bear...but Pawnee couldn't see the expression on Ezra's face as he stood behind her.

"It's so beautifully done!" she exclaimed, when the tour was over and they were back in the office standing in front of the architect's model of the completed site. "It's so perfect! How many people is there going to be space for?"

"Twenty-four in the chalets and twelve in the central module. Thirty-six altogether," Gord said.

"And what about the high-rise hotel building? Where's that going to be?"

Gord shook his head. "The 'high-rise' is what we call the two-storey part of the central block. That's all there is."

Pawnee stared. "But in town they keep talking about concrete monstrosities and high-rises and all that! Do people know what you're actually building?"

Ezra frowned. "I think they do. They must. McNab must have shown people the model, didn't he, Gord?"

Gord shrugged. "He showed it to his investors, I know that much, because I had to be here. I don't know who would have seen it locally."

Pawnee shook her head. "Well, if people could see this, see that the site really isn't being destroyed, see all those trees out there that you're going to replant when the work's over...I mean, Ezra, you maybe don't hear what I hear. People don't know who I am, half the time they think I'm off a yacht when I go shopping. So I hear a lot of what they're saying about this place. I think most people on the island really believe it's going to be a ten-storey pink concrete thing standing on the beach."

They decided to call it *Stage One Complete* and throw an all-afternoon party for anyone who cared to board the company ferry, come out to the site, drink a little champagne and examine the architect's model. Naturally no one would be allowed further up than the office, because the company didn't want to be sued for damages if anyone fell anywhere on the unfinished site. But from the office it was easy to see that the full picture was going to be as the model promised. Lots of trees had been removed, but they were lying prominently under damp tarpaulins on one side of the beach with their roots neatly bound, and everyone was primed to point out that their fate was to be restored to the hillside among the cabins when the work was finished.

The waterfall, being the first thing completed, would be the big winner, Pawnee was sure. Whatever the residents had heard about the "giant swimming pool" that was being built, they could not have dreamed that it would be anything so beautiful.

It had all happened very quickly. To delay meant to risk another "accident," maybe a more successful one. Tuesday had been the day of Pawnee's visit to the site, Saturday was the day of the party.

It hadn't taken long to explain matters to Barney McNab and get his agreement. Organizing the ferry trips and times from various locations, getting the word out, and getting the site in the best possible order for visitors had been Ezra's full-time preoccupation for three days.

And Pawnee's and Sonia's. The women had talked about the party at the hairdresser's, at the tennis courts, at the scuba school and in the boutiques.

Of course, Pawnee and Sonia would be there, adding the feminine touch, which everyone was careful not to put into words, but which all felt would be helpful.

''And I think it means a new dress!'' Sonia announced on Friday.

It said a lot for Pawnee's acclimatization that Sonia didn't have to argue. For the first time in her life Pawnee had learned how important clothes can be to the way people judge one, and for the first time, too, thanks to Ezra's constant generosity, she had the means to buy them. And she *wanted* a new dress. She wanted to be a help to Ezra on Saturday, and she was also determined to buy something so earthshakingly attractive that he would forget his scruples about making love to his own wife...

She'd thought about it long and hard, and had finally come to the conclusion that he could only have had one reason for pushing her away, and that was, that he didn't want to complicate their agreement. And sex would certainly complicate it.

The problem was, sex or no sex, it was already

deeply complicated for Pawnee. She loved Ezra. She was pretty sure that he was sexually attracted to her. And she figured that for a man at least, that could lead to love.

She was married to him, after all. Didn't she have some kind of right to try to seduce her own husband?

The dress she found took even Sonia's breath away. And the salesgirl said simply, "Well! I guess that was made for you in heaven."

"I've had a phone call from Barney," Beth told Pawnee that evening as she laid the table for one. "I guess you know he and his wife are coming out for this thing tomorrow. They're bringing a guest, too, some kind of celebrity."

"I understand," said Pawnee. The message was: Please don't use the swimming pool while the guest is in residence.

Ezra had said he wouldn't be home for dinner. He was busy supervising arrangements at the site. But he was glad of it. He didn't want to be in too close a proximity to Pawnee while all this was going on. He wanted the business out of his hair so that he could concentrate on Pawnee. Concentrate on overcoming his wife's deserved resentment at how he'd treated her, and get her into bed.

Next morning, too, he only grabbed a hasty coffee before heading off again. That suited Pawnee, who had plans of her own for the seduction of her husband.

First, a long, cool bath in the scented oils she had learned to love, that made her now dusty-gold skin so silky. Yesterday, at the salon getting their hair

trimmed, she and Sonia had had a manicure and ped-
icure, too, and both toe and fingernails were perfectly
glossed with warm pink polish.

She washed her hair again and put conditioner into
it, feeling how healthy it was now, and how easily it
fell into place, a glossy, glowing cap...

Her underwear was composed of what must be the
most expensive few square inches of cobweb ever
spun. Pawnee blushed when she put it on, but nothing
was going to stop her, not even her own shyness. If
this party went well today, Ezra would be happy, re-
lieved, and grateful to her. This was her chance, and
she intended to take it.

There was the sound of a truck arriving, and Pawnee slipped on a robe and rushed to open the door.

"Hi!" she said, and the young woman piling out
of the vehicle with two big cases that looked like
fishing tackle boxes returned the greeting.

"We've got lots of time," she said, entering the
house and following Pawnee to the bedroom. "I allowed extra, just in case. Hope I'm not too early for
you."

Pawnee shook her head and sat down in front of
her dressing table. Rough-hewn and unpolished, it
was a piece of furniture that looked as though it had
been carved out of driftwood. "Gosh, this place is
gorgeous! Is the hotel really going to be like this?"
exclaimed Holly, as she set down her cases and
snapped them open to reveal a spread of colours and
textures, brushes and pots.

So far sunk was Pawnee in the life of idleness and
luxury, she had even booked one of the salon's
makeup artists to come and do her makeup.

"Make me beautiful," she pleaded now, and Holly raised one expert eye and grinned.

"Not difficult," she said. "You should see some of the cases I've had. It'll be a pleasure to do such young skin."

The process seemed to go on forever. First, of course, Holly had to see the dress, to choose her tones and shades to match. When the "ohhing" and admiring were over, Pawnee sat fascinated as her face and neck were first cleansed, and then lathered with moisturizer, and then dabbed with various creams and foundations of different shades...

"There!" said Holly at last, drawing the towel from around Pawnee's neck, and the band from her hair. Pawnee sat up and took a deep breath before looking into the mirror. Then she sighed with delighted astonishment.

For the past ten minutes she had begun to think that she was going to look painted, overdone, so many brushstrokes had covered her face. But she need not have feared. She looked as if she weren't wearing any makeup at all. She merely glowed. Even around her eyes, the liner and pale green shadow was so subtly done that no mere male would understand how much of that delicate emphasis was art. Even her lips looked only pinkly wet.

"You're amazing," Pawnee breathed.

Holly laughed. "It's all you, really. All I do is point out who you really are. Let's put your dress on and see the total effect."

The dress, caught snug over the breasts and then all flowing panels to midcalf, was the softest, softest silk, in the colours of an English summer. Palest greens, pinks, yellows and blues washed over each other like wildflowers in a hedgerow. Out of this confection rose Pawnee's naked, smoky gold shoulders, slim but rounded, and her dark, vibrant head with its cap of clinging curls. In front of her small ears, two locks of hair curved into the hollow of her cheekbones, and above them, her dark eyes seemed exotically slanted.

It was as though one of Pan's fauns had wrapped herself in a leafy meadow to masquerade as a human. In her ears, Pawnee fastened tiny jewel flowers, on her feet, soft green leather sandals. She wore nothing else.

Apart from her wedding ring, which she had polished till it glowed.

"My golly!" Holly exclaimed as they moved onto the balcony. "When the wind blows, that dress hugs you as though you're not wearing anything." The silk, lovingly embracing each firm curve, seemed to define the neat musculature of the body better than nudity could.

Pawnee only looked in the mirror once. She was terrified that if she looked too long, she'd be afraid to go. When Holly had been given a tour of the house and had left, she waited nervously for Sonia to come and pick her up. Oh, if only her nerve held!

Ezra was drinking and listening to Beth's husband on the subject of farming when he caught sight of Pawnee coming through the door of the construction hut.

If ever a woman had looked out of his reach, his wife looked it then. He had never seen her look so much as if she belonged with the wealthy yachting crowd, and he realized with a hideous sinking feeling that there would be a lot of rich men here today. If she wanted to go off to Japan or Tahiti on a fabulous yacht, how could he stop her?

She was smiling at Barry, a wide, curving smile, so that she seemed like some creature from a fairy tale, with pointed ears and slanting eyebrows, dancing on moonlit nights and disappearing before you could capture her... "Bert, excuse me," he said, probably rudely interrupting, but he didn't even know if Bert was still talking or had finished and was waiting for a comment. "That's my wife."

"Good golly," said Bert, turning.

The crowd parted before Ezra like the Red Sea, for no doubt the sea parted, not as a conscious act of obedience, but as a kind of instinctive response to some sensed power.

He had never looked so big as he did now, towering over this delicate, magical wife like Beauty and the Beast. He felt his own size, but not as something dangerous and cumbersome, something to fear. He felt that he could protect her against giants, that he could slay challengers with a look, that he could pick her up with one hand and carry her off to his cave, but that not even in a moment of insanity, would he ever hurt her. His strength was hers.

And hers was his. He was not fooled by the faun-like delicacy. She was still the same, tough-minded, hardened-to-the-saddle woman who had been going to offer herself as trade to terrorists to free a sister. The contrast would fascinate him as long as he lived.

"Pawnee," he said softly. And then, because he

could, because she could not object here in front of strangers, because she was his very new wife and they all knew it, and lastly, because he damn well wanted to and couldn't stop himself, he wrapped one arm around her, pulled her helplessly against him and kissed her, hungrily, full on the lips.

Her hand slipped up to his shoulder and involuntarily clung to the collar of his shirt, and she opened her mouth tenderly under his, offering him her innocence.

By the time he could manage to let her go people were gently applauding. He took hold of her wrist so tightly it felt like a handcuff, but not one that Pawnee wanted to get out of. Her heart was beating, her skin was singing like a harp, and she just couldn't stop smiling up at him.

Now she leaned against his arm as he moved through the increasing numbers of people, now he felt how she confided herself to him. His blood was leaping crazily in his system, and it required a good deal of concentration to keep his body from advertising to the world that he'd rather be elsewhere.

They were a formidable pair. All the men looked from Pawnee's glowing, intriguing sexuality to the architect's model and were convinced. All the women looked from Ezra's rugged young bulk to the architect's model, and likewise were convinced.

"That's right, real thatch," Ezra pointed out. "We'll be bringing in expert thatchers from Wales. You know they still roof with thatch in parts of Wales and Devon."

"Yes, the water filtration system of the pool is solar powered, we had to develop a..."

Oh, yes, it must be true what they said about Barney McNab, that he was a capitalist who cared, a man who put the earth before profits, a real *Canadian*. And how wonderfully in keeping with its surroundings the hotel was, and that pool! How marvellous to be invited to come and inaugurate the pool on the day when construction was complete on the site...how enticing to think that Pawnee would be there in something even more revealing, that Ezra would be there with bare chest...

"No, he did plan to come," Ezra was explaining about the owner of all this. "His wife Jade Sweet was coming, too, she's the CCN anchorwoman, you know, and another Canadian celebrity, I don't know who. But there was a blizzard in Toronto again yesterday, and nothing could get off the ground at all."

"Oh, that's really too bad!" It was the yachting crowd who were most disappointed to miss the McNabs. The McNabs were part of wealthy society, of course they had a yacht, but because they worked so hard, and were somewhat reclusive, they were rarely met with. The islanders, on the other hand, had often met him on his visits. "Will they come when the blizzard lifts?"

"No, not now they've missed this shindig," Ezra explained, for so McNab's secretary had told him. He wished McNab had made it, because then maybe he himself wouldn't have had to stay to the bitter end, as he knew he must.

"I've got to stay," he muttered to Pawnee once, as yet another ferry load arrived.

"I know," she smiled. She wasn't in a hurry—or perhaps, she was in a hurry, but also nervous. In fact, she felt like a bride. Full of jitters. She was a virgin, but did he know that? Would he guess? Should she tell him? She took another gulp of the champagne that was flowing so freely.

He was so big, a giant of a man. What if it hurt? Would he understand? What if she changed her mind at the last minute? What if there was something wrong with her? What if she didn't know what to do *at all?*

So she would think, standing beside him as her husband chatted to this person and that, building herself to a little panic…and then he would turn and smile down at her with such loving eyes, such confident determination to make love to her that even a virgin like herself understood the message, and knew that she could safely leave the mechanics to him.

Everybody else in the room also got the message, and at last, out of pity, the last guests bade them goodbye and boarded the last ferry.

Of course the office was a shambles. Glasses everywhere, and the architect's model askew, and salmon and caviar trodden underfoot.

"You go on, Ez," Barry urged. "I've got a couple of the guys lined up to help with this. We don't need you. Terrific success, eh? Pawnee should get a company bonus."

It was sunset. Pawnee and Ezra, without speaking, wandered down onto the beautiful white stretch of beach to watch the sun disappear.

"Look," said Pawnee. "The tide's out. The path is there. Let's walk home that way."

He looked at her and knew that he'd walk through the sea to China if she asked. Common sense told him they were maybe both a little too loaded with champagne for this journey, but the champagne overrode the common sense, and Ezra bent over, rolled up his pant legs and took off his deck shoes as Pawnee slipped carefully out of her sandals and bent to pick them up.

"Oooh, wow!" she said softly. "I've had more of that champagne than I thought." She took his hand, though, and paddled through the pool that the retreating tide had left between the beach and the exposed sandbar. The breeze caught her dress as they walked, blowing it softly against his legs, and against her body.

Suddenly it was all there, just as Miranda had said: sunset, sand and sea...the scent of perfume. A yacht sailing by to safe harbour at Port Sunrise was playing a haunting, seductive song that murmured over the water like a woman wailing for her demon lover. They stood silently, listening and watching as the ship passed, and the tide turned, and the sun set into darkness.

And now it was a savage place, holy and enchanted. The water was brushing gently over their feet with the incoming tide, and they stirred and moved to walk on. Pawnee turned to look up at Ezra in the starlight, and fell into the ocean.

Funny, he'd been thinking, *what you could learn just standing on a night like this and watching the sun set. Funny that a moment like this could tell you what you should have realized long ago—that the feeling that half killed you when you looked at your wife was love.*

When she fell, it was as if the sea, in answer to his thoughts, had decided to steal her from him. Though there was little danger, Ezra had never moved so quickly in his life as he did to catch Pawnee from its greedy grasp. Bending, he caught her arm, and then her waist, and then he picked her up high and dripping in his arms, and strode through the foaming dark water and the magical black night to take his wife home to bed.

11

———▶◀———

On the shore of the wide world Ezra stood thinking.
Twelve hours ago he had faced the other way, while
the sun had gone down. Now it had made its reap-
pearance on the other side of the world. Ezra felt the
inevitability of nature's rhythm strum through his
own being, and nodded, as though someone had said
something.

He understood that the ancient Greeks had been
right: Apollo and his fiery cart went down into the
underworld at night. And last night, while the sun had
been in the earth's depths, Ezra had been in his own.

He had met the animal within, fully, for the first
time in his life. It had roared and prowled and leapt
and lashed its tail...

He had been ferocious with her. He had treated
Pawnee the way he had never treated a woman before
in his life. Always before he had kept his animal under strict control, but not last night. Last night it
would not have been possible. If he had wrestled with
it, he would have lost the battle. Instead he had ridden
it, carried by its wildness to places he had not realized
existed, taking Pawnee with him.

He had heard music all the while, as though her

body sang a song for him. That song had been his guide—his hands and his body, his mouth, had built the song to a wild, crashing crescendo, like a torrent of waves on a beach…and he had learned then that it was a song he had been waiting to hear all his life.

Of course he had known it before, only he had been too stupid to understand. On his wedding day, putting the gold band onto her finger, he had known it then, had felt it deep within, though he had not understood the feeling…

She had been a virgin. He would remember all his life the moment when he had realized it. Before that, he had heard surprise in her cries, the grateful surprise that comes as pleasure makes its first journey through the sexual pathways…but he thought it meant she had met only with clumsy lovers. He had cursed their masculine stupidity and greed and at the same time had become more and more determined to give her all the pleasure she had been robbed of before…

And then at last, he had entered, and found the way barred, and her cry was half-shock, half-amazement, and so was his own. He had stopped, and put his hand under her neck and held her head till her eyes, drunk with the wild mix of pain and pleasure, focused on him. "Pawnee," he whispered hoarsely. "Pawnee."

She had smiled at him with a smile he would remember all his life. "It's all right," she'd murmured softly. "I knew it would hurt a little."

That was when the animal within had leapt into full, triumphant stride. An animal guided by only two things—her song of pleasure, and his own. And when the two songs blended and became one wild, thundering symphony in which the orchestra of the whole world took part, Ezra had, for the first time in his life, stood face-to-face with the ramping, roaring beast he had feared, and understood that it was not his cross but his glory.

Had understood that until that moment, he, too, had been a virgin.

Now the breeze blew the hair from his brow, and the sun climbed further up the sky, and the water further up the beach below, and Ezra felt the first stirrings of doubt. He wondered how perfect his memory of last night was. It was not the champagne that worried him, but the way he had been drunk on passion. She had been new to it: Had he scared her? Had it been too much for a first time? If he'd known earlier... So easy, he told himself—now, when it was too late—so easy to think you were taking a woman with you...was that what his grandfather had been talking about?

Of course, he could overcome her fears in time. But if he had scared her last night, how much would that work against him when he came to tell his wife that he loved her, that he wanted her for life, and that if she kept him to their bargain it would kill him?

"Ezraaaa! Ezzzzzra!" the voice carolled from behind him, down from the house, with cheerful but impersonal good humour. He could hardly believe his ears. He might have expected anything except that tone of cool friendliness, and he squeezed his eyes shut in response to the urgent clenching of his heart. If she had decided to be a stranger, how would he deal with it?

"Ez!" He felt the footsteps through the earth, and turned at last to meet her.

"Cree!" he shouted, his jaw dropping in astonishment. And then, disbelief coming second, *"Cree?"*

She ran down the last few feet and straight into his arms, wrapping her own around his waist to give him an exuberant hug. "Hi!" she said excitedly. "Surprised to see me?"

"Very," he commented dryly. He returned the hug, and then she stepped back and grinned up at him. "Where the heck did you spring from?"

"Ah, you wouldn't believe it, Ez! I was supposed to be with Barney McNab and Jade Sweet, but they're not coming now!" Ezra suddenly remembered that Barney McNab owned CCN. "The plane schedule was all shot to pieces by the weather, I didn't arrive till really late last night. Golly, isn't this place fantastic? You have to see it to believe it! Where's Pawnee? Is she still asleep? I didn't want to come down till a more civilised hour, but then I saw you down here on the beach. Will she mind if I wake her?"

Somewhere he felt sadness that he would not be waking his wife as he had meant to, gently, watching for the first expression in her eyes, that would tell him what he had to know.... Ezra turned with Cree and began the climb up to the house.

"No, she won't mind. We're usually up by now, even on a Sunday, but we had that party yesterday and both of us had a lot of champagne." Funny how ordinary you could make the most important day of your life sound. *I made love to my wife last night and I am changed forever.* He tried that out in his head. No, you couldn't say a thing like that out loud...except maybe to your wife, if she looked as if she wanted to hear it...

He thought, with sudden urgency, *I can still do it. I'll go in and wake her, we can have a minute or two together, and that's all it will take to know...*

"Cree?" cried a voice from above, in drowsy excitement. Pawnee stood above them on the terrace, staring down as they emerged from the foliage. "Cree, what are you—how on *earth* did you get here?" and then the sisters were laughing and hugging and exchanging unintelligible cries, sounding like birds over the sea.

He was standing just behind Cree. Pawnee could have looked at him if she'd wanted to. But she didn't look anywhere except at her sister.

Damn, damn, damn.

A sheep was caught in a gate, and called out to her...

When she awoke the room was filled with sunlight, and so was her body. Pawnee felt as if her blood were melted gold, as if the light that played on her skin came as much from within as without.

Movies told you nothing. Other people told you nothing. They all made it sound like a really good meal out or something. But it was a lot more than that. It was walking through the Valley of the Shadow of Death and fearing no evil. It was facing the source of Light and of Love and finding the two the same. It was knowing that, on some level, she and Ezra were the same...*one.* It was religion and paradise all at once.

Now she was one with Ezra. To be divided from him now would break not just her, but some essential connection of the universe. As though mankind was a radio receiver for divine grace. Too many broken connections, no matter how small, and eventually the radio would stop receiving.

Slowly, Pawnee returned to ordinary consciousness, and turned to the empty pillow beside her head, and blushed, remembering how abandoned he had made her. She had thought of nothing but her own pleasure, she had showed him a part of her that she herself had never before met…she had been completely without shame then, but now…

She remembered that something had awakened her. A cry that in her dream she had heard as a sheep in the barnyard gate. But there were no sheep here, and there were no birds crying now. What…had it been Ezra? Where was he?

Her beautiful dress lay in a little heap on the floor, and Pawnee felt the heat burn her cheeks again when she remembered its coming off. How would he look at her? She stepped over it and, reaching for her beach dress that lay on a chair, pulled it over her naked body. Then she went into the lounge and glanced nervously about her. He was not here. She went onto the balcony.

The foliage around the path was stirring with the passage of someone, and Pawnee shivered and braced herself. Had she—had he…last night, he had stopped when he knew, and looked at her, and said her name in a way that turned her brain, what was left of it, to mush, her blood to steam. She had been so lost. What had she said then? Had she told him? Was that why he'd got up without waking her?

And then the sound of a woman's voice, burbling

happily, was brought to her ears, and then she was staring with utter incredulity at Cree.

"It is really, seriously weird to become famous overnight but not for anything you've *done*," Cree told them over breakfast on the balcony a little later. "Hey, this is fabulous! This is paradise!" she breathed deeply, a Canadian released from the prison of winter, and the other two were both abruptly reminded of what they had left so short a time before. Somehow, in a climate like this, the state of "blizzard" came to seem unreal, no more than a bad dream. Cree's pale greed for the sun's heat made them shiver, as if with the recognition of their own mortality.

"What's it been like?" Pawnee asked, afraid to let the conversation drift. She found it absolutely impossible to look at Ezra. Sometimes she felt him look at her, but she just couldn't. Not now. When they were alone.

"Well, maybe it's different for an actress or a singer, or someone who's written a book, I wouldn't know. For me, it's just weird. I go on these talk shows, they send reporters and photographers to interview me—I even opened the new wing of a high school, can you believe that? And I had to talk to the assembled student body about 'courage under pressure.'"

"Golly, what on earth did you say?"

"I said that that was the subject I'd been asked to address, but that my experience hadn't required the kind of courage that other hostages had needed, so I was the wrong one to ask. I said that the courage I had learned about was the courage of those women in the little village where I was held, who had to fight daily against a hostile land…well,'' Cree sniffed and grinned. ''You don't want to hear all that. I have to say it's been a lot of fun, and I've been getting to meet some people you normally only read about—it's really weird how you just get accepted into the ranks of celebrities!''

''Really,'' said Pawnee. Ezra wasn't saying much. She wished he would. Maybe she could have read something from his tone. But he just sat there, watching the two sisters, and every minute that passed made it more impossible to look directly at him.

Cree sighed and looked around, at the foliage, the sky, the sea. ''No one told me how fabulous this is.''

Later they went into Port Sunrise for lunch at an exclusive brasserie frequented by the yachting crowd. It was the kind of place Pawnee knew Cree would enjoy, but she hadn't reckoned on the reaction. Several caramel-skinned people with more gold than was good for them hanging from their wrists and necks came up to the table because they recognized Cree, and congratulated her on her bravery and her escape. Most of them were Canadians.

''I had no *idea* she was your *sister,*'' said a woman whose yacht Pawnee had visited for sundowners a few days before. ''Why didn't you tell us?''

''I never thought of it,'' Pawnee admitted. She grinned at Cree.

''You must come for drinks. Do come for drinks,'' the woman insisted. Her smile included the three of them, pausing with interest on Ezra and then flicking back to Pawnee as if to say, ''You didn't mention *him* either." "Tonight. Are you free for dinner aboard? We do have the most marvellous chef. I don't know why we ever come ashore!"

"Thanks, not tonight," said Cree firmly. "Thank you very much, but I haven't seen my sister for ages."

"Tomorrow, then. I'll expect you all about six, and we'll sail out a little and watch the sunset."

Cree wasn't quite as adept as she'd thought. With no other excuse ready, she lacked the courage just to be rude.

"I am sorry about that," she muttered, when the women had gone back to her own table, covered with the complacency of success. "Isn't it ridiculous?" She turned her hands up. "I haven't done a thing except in the passive. I got taken hostage, and I was released."

"And you signed an exclusive contract with Barney McNab," Pawnee pointed out.

Cree giggled. "I know. And he paid me, I can tell you! I don't say I could buy you a farm, Pawnee, but I can sure do something. And I've met a lot of people with a lot of money lately, and some of them don't know what the hell to do with it. So let's think about that. We could probably get some financing for a little business or something."

Pawnee's eyes fell, then she quickly forced her gaze back up to her sister's, and smiled. "Great!" she said lightly.

He'd been patient, waiting, letting her have the time she needed...but now Ezra turned to stone where he sat. The paralysis started in his chest and moved outwards to his head and all his extremities. All he could do was sit there like two eyes in a mountain and stare at Cree and wish he could throttle her. Or something.

"I mean, none of this is going to last forever. I'll be last week's news soon. And you aren't going to be here longer than a few months, are you? So let's do the best we can with my good luck while we've got it."

Pawnee glanced at Ezra at last. She almost said, *What do you think, Ezra?* but his face was absolutely impassive. Not by a look or a word did he indicate that her future might be of interest to him, and she looked away again. "Yeah, we'll think of something," she said. Now she knew why she hadn't been able to look at Ezra before. She'd had to wait till she could bear to see that last night had been meaningless to him.

Thus it was that, later, at the other house, when the two sisters were alone and Cree asked, "So, what's the scoop on you and Ezra? Are you getting it together yet?"

Pawnee took a deep breath and said, "Of course not."

"Of course not? Of *course* not? Are you crazy? Are you seriously sitting there telling me that you intend to let this terrific guy go to waste?"

Pawnee paused, groping for words.

"Consider me a large ear," Cree invited.

Pawnee shook her head. "There's nothing to tell. It's a business deal, Cree! That's all it ever was and that's all it's ever going to be!" And then, remembering his bland, hard face this afternoon, her heart kicked in protest. Not by a word, not by the flicker of one eyelash, had he indicated that he had plans of his own for Pawnee's future. She had thought it was all decided, but that just showed what a fool she was. For her it had been precious, but not for him.

But then, she'd been a virgin. She supposed for Ezra it had been just another sexy woman in a list, and who knew how long the list was? Cree was right in what she implied, probably Ezra could have any woman he wanted. Women were always throwing themselves at him, she'd seen it even in the short time they'd been here. Yesterday at the site they'd been staring at him like a pack of hungry wolves, united in their predatory interest. And the richer they were, she'd noticed, the more likely they were to look at Ezra in that way.

So last night had meant nothing more than this: She'd thrown herself at him and he'd obligingly taken her to bed.

Out of her pain, she overrode Cree's protest with a "Don't you see how complicated it would make everything if we...if we started anything? What if one of us fell for the other, and the other one didn't?"

Cree looked at her. "Has he fallen for you? I can believe it, the way you look! You look utterly gorgeous, Pawnee. Is that the problem? You're trying to keep him at arm's length? Do you *really* not feel attracted to him?"

Pawnee said, "No," in answer to every question but the last, but the timing was such that Cree took it as an answer to the last one.

She sat back. "Boy, you're hard to please! Have you found someone rich, a yachtie, is that it?"

"No," said Pawnee again. And somehow there was no way back to the previous moment, no way she could say, even to her own sister, *It's not him who loves me, it's me who loves him...*

"Well, the way you look, I'm amazed. I have never seen you looking so fabulous, it just shows what a little money can do. You *look* as though you're in love, honey, you just glow! What have you been doing, and can money buy it?"

It was a relief to get off the subject of Ezra. It was a relief to stay up talking till one o'clock, and then to spend that night with Cree at the McNab house rather than go where she wanted to go—home to Ezra. It was a relief to tire herself out with talking, so that she didn't have to think.

Ezra did not tire himself out with talking, nor with anything else. He waited for Pawnee to return, hour after hour, until it dawned on him that she wasn't coming home. That this was her final word on what had happened last night.

He stood out on the far reaches of the terrace, from where, above him on the cliff, he could just see the lights of the McNab house through the greenery. He stood there until all the lights went out, and a few minutes longer, fighting with disbelief and anger.

Then he went and pulled a bottle of malt whisky out of the bar, and a glass, and sat down and looked out over the same sea he'd stared at this morning, and drank until he fell asleep.

12

"I've got an idea," said Cree over coffee the next morning.

The guest house had been built so as to be almost completely hidden from the terrace of the house above, but that didn't stop Pawnee from staring down at the roof in the trees below as if it held the answer to her troubles. They had talked late, and slept late. Ezra would already be at the site.

"I *said,* I've got an idea."

"Great. What's your idea?"

"I'm going to take Ezra off your hands."

"You're—" Pawnee put her hand to her chest and swallowed with difficulty. She shook her head, and looked at her sister. "Sorry, that went down the wrong way. What?"

"It's a great idea, isn't it? I've always liked Ezra, and the poor guy! We can't leave him pining when he was our knight in shining armour."

My knight in shining armour, Pawnee wanted to protest. But she sat speechless, watching her sister as though she were an inevitable phenomenon of nature. Well, she was.

"So, what do you think?"

"What do I think about what?"

"I just told you! About me being's Ezra's consolation prize."

Pawnee said carefully, "Ezra is not pining for me. He doesn't need a consolation prize."

"Even better! I must say, it goes against the grain with me to be anybody's second best, but for Ezra I was willing to make an exception," she laughed gaily.

"I'm sure you won't be second best with him," Pawnee said tonelessly. For a moment she wished, so hard she thought she would burst, that she had the right to lay claim to him, to say, *he's mine, hands off.* For a moment she considered saying, *I love him, please leave him alone.* But it was all too fresh. Once started, she would not be able to stop, she'd be crying out the whole pathetic tale. And she just couldn't bear to discuss Saturday night with anyone, not even Cree, whom she loved...

"What are you going to wear tonight?" she asked instead.

"So Ezra, I came just in time, right?"

Pawnee was in the sea. Ezra had come home from work, and they had come down as usual for their evening dip, prior to dressing for the dinner aboard a yacht that none of them really wanted to attend.

With fierce and dogged precision, Ezra had swum out almost to the mouth of the bay and then back in. Cree had followed him up out of the water. He was rubbing his head vigorously with the towel. He paused. "Just in time for what?"

She smiled playfully at him. "Well, now, we can't

have you falling for Pawnee and messing up a purely business arrangement, can we? Never mix business with pleasure, Ezra, haven't you heard that?"

"I've heard it."

"Well, there you go!" she twinkled, but he was not smiling.

Suddenly Ezra seemed twice his usual size. Cree flinched, not so sure any more that she wanted to play games with Ezra.

"Did your sister complain?" he asked, in cold, level tones. But he knew the answer. She must have. Not even sparky little Cree would be taking after him like this without Pawnee's permission.

He wanted to break rocks with his bare hands. He wanted to tear the cliff down and throw it into the ocean.

"Pawnee hasn't said anything," Cree answered in sudden alarm.

"No?" He was nodding in complete disbelief. "You just picked it up, did you? Sisterly intuition?"

"Something like that." He looked full at her, then, his face still unmoving, but now she saw it in his eyes. It was like seeing a mountain crumble. Her first guess had been right—Ezra had fallen for Pawnee. Fallen hard.

Cree gasped a lungful of air, but before she could form any words, Ezra had turned on his heel and was striding away, up towards the house.

Pawnee dressed in nearly the same outfit she had worn on Saturday afternoon, but the ritual of dressing couldn't have seemed more different, even though she washed the salt out of her hair, and rubbed cream into

her skin, and made up in much the same way. The
feeling in her heart then had been excited anticipation.
Now she felt like wood.

A horrified Beth had carefully washed and ironed
the salt-encrusted silk this afternoon, and the dress
had survived. Pawnee pulled it on and slipped into a
pair of gold sandals, because one of the pretty green
ones had been lost in the sea when Ezra had lifted
her so firmly into his arms…

She picked up the little flower earrings and her
heart clenched with the memory of hope she had
felt…she set them back in the case and pulled out a
bangly gold pair that were more suitable to the evening ahead.

An evening in hell. What would she do? How could
she look at him? Would he want her again, and if he
did, what could she say?

She could not say yes. She couldn't let him make
love to her when to her it was everything and to him
only amusement.

But she could never say no. If he looked at her
with even one degree of the need she felt, she would
fall at the first fence.

She waited for him on the terrace. He seemed to
shower for a long time; they would be late. They
would miss sunset from the sea, it would be over
before the boat could get underway.

Pawnee was glad. Maybe it would be better for her
if she never watched another sunset with Ezra, even
in company.

He watched her turn as he stepped onto the terrace.
She was wearing the thing she'd worn the other night,
the thing all silk and flowers that he could remember

so clearly taking from that perfect, lithe body…that body that he could remember taking more pleasure from than he'd felt in the whole total of his life before. He clenched his teeth, to stop himself shouting at her. What was there to say? *Why wasn't it right for you? Why did you pretend to love it so much, everything I did made you moan…*

Women were inexplicable, after all. Why hadn't she told him, instead of pretending? Why…he heaved a sigh, forcing his thoughts to stop.

"Ready?" he said.

She nodded, bent to pick up a scarf and an evening bag and preceded him from the house. They picked up Cree at the top.

"Hi," was all she said as she climbed in. It wasn't like Cree to be so subdued, but the other two scarcely noticed. They were only grateful. They were so consumed with their own thoughts that conversation would have been all but impossible.

They drove to Port Sunrise without exchanging a word. None of them was aware of the silence.

Their hostess had invited half the inhabitants of the yachts in Port Sunrise to meet the Canadian hostage, of whose existence by now even the Americans were aware.

Drinks were already flowing freely by the time the guest of honour arrived, and the Helbigs had decided not to bother sailing anywhere. They had a nice little berth out in the harbour; they'd watch the sunset through the masts of all the sailing yachts.

"How dare they take a Canadian!" Sylvia Helbig railed to Cree. "We've never done anyone any harm, and there are so many Shamsirabians in Canada! All of them for economic reasons, I'm sure.''

Cree shrugged, but no response was necessary. Sylvia was talking enough for both of them. "What have we ever done to the citizens of Shamsirabia? It was Canadian engineers who developed the method to put out all those oil rig fires that Saddam Hussein started, for goodness' sake! Don't they know that?''

"That was in Kuwait," Cree pointed out gently.

"Well?" said Sylvia, with an indignant shrug. "It's all the same, isn't it?''

Cree rolled her eyes.

Ezra knew he must be commenting in all the right places. The woman was talking in a low, soothing voice, very firmly, and gazing deeply and determinedly into his eyes. She was only lightly tanned, even less wrinkled, with long, smooth blond hair, and jewellery that marked her as someone who had long ago been a hippie, who might be rich now, but who prided herself on never having sold out.

"The truth is, it's women who make the decisions in matters sexual," she was saying. "Women always have the upper hand, if they want it. But most women want things the other way. They want to be pursued." Her eyes flicked lightly down to his chest and back up again. "It's foolish of them, don't you think?''

Pawnee didn't want to be pursued, he guessed. He wished she did, but she'd made her feelings pretty clear. Asking her own sister to tell him... Staring at nothing, Ezra told himself his grandfather had been right after all. He should never have shown her his need, that hot, painful desire...the need that was burning in his gut like acid right now. He should have kept it hidden. He smiled and nodded to the ghost of his grandfather. *You got the last laugh, you old hypocrite.*

"Wonderful," said the deep-voiced, sexually confident predator in front of him in satisfaction, and stared even more deeply into his eyes. Belatedly Ezra realized that he might have nodded in the wrong place.

Someone turned the lights in the saloon down low, and he was suddenly looking straight through the glass doors at his wife. On deck in plain view, and letting some damned playboy paw her.

"How long have you been married?"

Pawnee stared down into her drink. Maybe if she drank enough of this stuff it would act as a painkiller? She took another gulp. No effect so far. "We got married last month," she said. She drank again.

"So recently?" He sounded so astonished that Pawnee involuntarily looked up. He was a good-looking man, and well-preserved, with a tan that had been packed on like brown sugar on a ham. She dropped her eyes again. "You look discontented enough for it to have been at least six months ago." He laughed gently at his own wit. He was English, very upper crust, very wealthy, if the whispers she'd overheard when he arrived were correct.

"I'm not discontented," she said softly into her drink. She could not afford emphasis. Anything might bring on tears tonight.

"Not?" A tanned hand came up and touched her chin, forcing it up. The touch was essentially mas-

culine, determined and in control, and it reminded her
of Ezra's, Saturday night, when he had been so sure,
so expert, making her sure, too.

She opened her eyes at him, feeling them fill with
unwanted tears, unable to control them. He drew in a
quick breath, as though the sight caught unexpectedly
at him. "I can take you away, you know," he murmured softly, his hand not leaving her chin. "We can
up anchor at first light and disappear."

With sudden inconsequence she remembered his
name. On a half laugh, she protested, "Dominic—"

"Take your hands off my wife," a voice growled
just above his right ear.

Dominic Parton turned with impeccable calm and
lifted his eyes to Ezra's face. "Certainly," he said,
and, suiting the action to the word, dropped his hand
and slipped it into his jacket pocket. "But only one
was on her, dear boy. It wasn't a serious assault."

"And it won't be," said Ezra grimly, not giving
an inch.

Parton paused. "Quite," he said, moving his head
in a little nod. He turned to Pawnee, one eyebrow
raised. "My dear, I am not at all averse to doing battle
in your honour. You have only to say the word. He
is big, but they do, I understand, fall hard."

She couldn't have joked to save her life. She didn't
understand anything except that Ezra was looking like
a bear with a seriously sore head standing under a
thundercloud, and her own heart was beating like a
bunch of cows crossing a tin bridge.

What on earth was the matter with Ezra? Surely he
didn't seriously think… She shook her head quickly
at Dominic, her lower lip between her teeth, and, her

gaze falling on her glass again, took another healthy swig of the contents. She was pretty sure it was a very good champagne. She'd heard someone say, "Ah" in satisfied tones when they'd looked at the label, but here she was drinking it like pop.

"That's sure to give you courage," Dominic Parton commented without apparent irony. "I'll leave you, then, my dear."

There was silence between them. Nervously, Pawnee drained the last of the sparkling liquid in her glass. Before she could move, someone in white shorts and a black polo shirt with the yacht's logo on the breast was there pouring a refill. She gulped some down.

"You'll make yourself sick," said Ezra.

She looked at him, suddenly feeling that Dominic had been right. It *was* giving her courage. "Will I?" she challenged.

"Either that, or just drunk enough to say yes to the next ageing cavalier who wants to rescue you on his gold-plated, velvet-trimmed oceangoing yacht."

"Ageing? He's probably forty!"

"That's twelve years older than me, and seventeen years older than you," Ezra pointed out, furiously.

He was angry. Why was he angry? She deliberately took another sip of champagne, and watched him over the rim of her glass. Was Ezra *jealous?* She smiled involuntarily at the thought.

"He's younger than most rich men," she pointed out. "And I understand he's not married."

The smug little smile infuriated him.

"Well, *you are!*"

Her heart started to climb up towards her throat in

little breath-stopping leaps, like a nimble goat above
a dangerously high valley. She stared at him. No word
would come to her. She drank again. He was so close,
too close. Why didn't he touch her? If only he would
put his hand on her, as Dominic had, just the tiniest
touch—she would know then.

"Aren't you?" he insisted.

His eyes were on fire, and she was melting in their
heat. Oh, God, she had to stop this. She was fanta-
sizing, seeing what she wanted to see, and she would
make a terrible fool of herself if she were wrong.

She tore her gaze away from his. He was too close,
how could she think when he was so close? Why
didn't he touch her? If he was jealous, why didn't he
say so?

"I'm sorry if I'm making people think your wife
is unfaithful," she muttered, clutching her glass with
both hands and bending to drink again.

He did touch her then; she got what she wanted.
He seized her wrist in a cool, merciless hold and pre-
vented her drinking. Her heart made the last, death-
defying leap into her throat, choking her, her blood
was rushing around as if she had her very own closed-
circuit waterfall, and she understood that she should
not have wished for him to touch her, because this
was the most dangerous thing of all.

"Do you think I give a damn what these people
think?" he ground out through a furiously clenched
jaw.

He pulled her hand to his lips and buried his mouth
in her palm. He was trembling, a lock of his thick
dark hair had fallen forward and she watched, her
blood pounding, the way it moved with his heartbeat.

He loves me. The thought blasted through her as though she'd been shot up with electricity. Everything went liquid in her, including her knees, but he was quick, as quick as he had been on the sandbar on Saturday, his arm snapping around her waist to support her, and then, involuntarily, drawing her body against his.

He was hard. His body pressed painfully against her. She knew what that meant, not just for him, but for her—she knew what unbelievable pleasure it promised her, and her own body melted into instant clamour for it. She pressed against him, tearing her hand from his mouth in order to wrap it around his neck.

He moaned and devoured her lips with his.

"Hate to interrupt," said an apologetic voice. "But maybe you don't know you're turning into the star attraction?"

The lights in the saloon were turned low, but not so low Ezra couldn't see that about twenty guests were staring their way, eyes wide open. Including the well-preserved blonde with whom, he was pretty sure, he'd just agreed to some assignation.

13

---◆---

"We're leaving," Pawnee whispered to Cree.

Cree glanced involuntarily at her watch. "It's only eight-thirty. They haven't served the food yet!" she hissed in surprise.

"I know. Do you mind staying? They won't mind us going if you stay. Somebody'll drive you home."

Cree would have loved to get away. She was in a bad mood tonight, but she knew what Pawnee said was true. She nodded, then looked at her sister. If they were leaving early, maybe—

"You know he loves you, Pawnee," she said softly. "And your incredibly slow sister has finally figured out that you're pretty desperate about him."

Pawnee smiled tremulously, not trusting anything to words yet. Cree said, "I made him think…I'm not sure what he thinks you told me. Tell him it's just pure, blind ignorance, won't you?"

Pawnee squeezed Cree's hand and was gone.

"Aren't the Arabs a terribly virile race?" a woman asked her, as if she really wanted to know.

"I was kept with the women," Cree said flatly. "And you get the prize!"

"Pardon me?"

"That's the one thousandth time someone's asked me that." She smiled brightly. "I've been counting."

Ezra got one of the crew to take them ashore in the dinghy without making a lot of noise about it, and when they got there he tipped the kid well. Rude it might be, but he was damned well going to have this out with his wife *now,* and surely there were enough people still aboard to eat up all the grub.

As they walked to the truck, the moon sailed out from behind a tiny cloud, full, fat, fresh; like new cream cheese. A breeze pulled her dress against her body. She looked even more elfin in moonlight, he noted. She was walking just a little ahead, and, feeling oddly superstitious, he reached out and caught her arm, reassuring himself with the feeling of her warm flesh, the pulse of blood beneath the surface.

At this touch she slowed her anxious pace to his.

Beside the car, she paused, waiting for him to find the key. He couldn't get over his awareness and sense of her mystery, as though he had found her in a forest clearing and wasn't really sure what she was. His hand closed on the key in his pocket, and the next thing he knew, he had her pressed up against the side of the truck and was kissing her in sudden, crazy hunger on the mouth.

"You're in my blood," he muttered, when it was a case of either lift his mouth or drag her down to the ground. "You're like wine in my blood and perfume in my nose and...dammit, *dammit!* Let's get out of here!"

He pressed his mouth to her shoulder as he spoke, and electricity sparked and jumped across different bits of her, so that she felt like a tangle of wires each connected to a different power source.

"Ezra," she whispered. The champagne hadn't done much to numb anything, but it was, apparently, a sexual stimulus conductor second to none. "Ezra."

He heard longing in her voice, and his body leapt in response. *Get the door open. You can make love to her in the car,* said the voice of crazy passion in his head. Ezra saw where he was heading and stepped back, removing both hands and all parts of his anatomy from contact with hers.

"We've got to get out of here, or I'm going to lose it," he told her.

"Ezra," she stuttered.

He held up his hands desperately. "No, don't say anything. Especially don't say my name." He put the key in the door and opened it.

"I love you," said Pawnee uncontrollably. "Do you love me? Tell me now. I can't drive all that way not knowing. It's all right if you don't, I'll be all right, but I have to know, Ezra. I have to know."

He thought his head was going to come off. He bent and kissed her mouth with the violence of the starving, lifted her bodily up, shoved her onto the seat and slammed the door.

Somehow he got around to the other side of the car, somehow he got in. He slammed the door again, swore with desperate violence, swept her into his arms, her ungentle giant, and pressed a kiss to her mouth so passionate the moon was blotted out.

Then he tore his mouth away from the feast, rammed the key into the ignition the way he wanted to ram himself into her, and started the car.

They drove in silence. He had not answered her question in words, but she was swamped by the passion of his response to it. The truck bounced roughly over the track, and then, at last, they were home. She slipped out of the car and stood waiting, and then he was beside her, his hand on her wrist, and she understood that his silence had been all urgency, and that he could no longer control it.

Ezra had never been so aroused in his life. He got her into the house, and slammed the door, and instantly dragged her against him, kissing her with the ferocity of a lion with its prey. The top of her dress came down under his hand's rough seeking, and her breast was covered with a pale, delicate cobweb that was no barrier against his wet, hungry mouth.

"I love you," he said, his mouth coming up again to devour hers. "Don't you know it? You know I love you, you're my *wife!*" The last word came out of his depths, as if torn by the roots. He kissed her throat, felt the pulse beating there.

He was lying down, with her on top of him. He must have got her to the bedroom, but he had no memory of the journey. The thin dress was no barrier against his wildly seeking body. He held her hips and pressed up against her. "Do I love you? What did you think?" He lifted his head and took her breast into his mouth, and when she cried out in passionate astonishment, his body leapt again. He held her firmly down, making her body take the impulse of his.

"Ezra," she whispered, half protest, half plea.

"Damn, I want you," he muttered into her throat. His hands were up under the skirt of the silky dress, feeling the skin of her thighs, and then the delicate cobweb of the lace covering what he wanted. He pulled the lace roughly aside and his fingers found the goal, a hot, moist home.

"Ahh!" She gasped in astonishment, and her eyes shut and her mouth opened, and her body leapt against his expert hand.

One hand he moved in her, with the other he held her body's electric centre against his own hardness, watching her face above him as she gasped out her involuntary, animal response to the still unfamiliar pleasure.

He shifted his body, so that she lay on the bed now, and he lay on one side over her. Then his thumb began to tease her flesh with such directness that she saw light in the darkness, shooting to all the corners of the room.

"You love me," he said urgently, watching hungrily as her mouth opened on too much pleasure.

"Yes," she cried.

"Say it," he ordered. "Say it!"

"I love you, Ezra. Oh, I love you so much."

"You're my wife. Say it."

"I'm your wife." On the word, the pleasure she had been seeking came to her, slowly, deliciously, like warm, sweet honey. "Oh, Ezra, oh my, oh, it's so sweet."

"And you will not leave me."

"Oh, oh, *ohhhhh, ohhhhh*, Ezra!"

"You will not leave me. Say it!"

"I...oh, Ezra..." She was panting now. "I won't leave you, if you don't want me to, Ezra, I love you, ah, Ezra..." she whispered.

He couldn't stand any more. He tore at his clothes,

and then his body was in the hot, wet embrace of hers, and he put his mouth on hers and drowned himself in her passion as her body heaved and trembled under his relentless embrace.

It was midnight, and the moon rode high over the thrush and sigh of the sea. They sat on the terrace in the night's cool embrace, lazily eating the meal they had put together.

In the pale moonlight she was still elfin and elusive, but now she was his. She had given her word, and he knew she would keep it.

"I should have known then," he said. "I should have known when I was putting that ring on your finger that it was no business deal. It was real for me even then."

She sighed and smiled at him.

"When you said you wouldn't come here with me, I should have known then that it was more than the job."

"You threatened to refuse to divorce me," she remembered with smiling satisfaction. "I was so angry, but I think even then, I secretly wanted to come with you. You said I'd be stuck with you."

"You are," he said. "For life."

She tilted her head in moonlight, and looked at him with an expression in her eyes that made his blood leap. "All right," she said.

He leaned over to kiss her. After a moment they looked out to sea again.

"It's lovely here, isn't it?" she said quietly.

Below them, the sea hissed and shushed in the magic darkness.

"It is."

"Is there anywhere else in the world as good as this?"

He shrugged. "Probably not."

"We've been lucky, then."

He sat in silence for a moment. "My luck started before that."

Her heart thumped. "Did it?"

"You know it did."

She smiled, feeling the tenderness of the night all around her. "Yes," she said, "so did mine."

* * * * *

MILLS & BOON

Emma Darcy

The Collection

✳ ✳ ✳ ✳

This autumn Mills & Boon® brings you a powerful
collection of three full-length novels by an
outstanding romance author:

Always Love
To Tame a Wild Heart
The Seduction of Keira

Over 500 pages of love, seduction and intrigue.

Available from September 1998

DEBBIE MACOMBER

Married in Montana

Needing a safe place for her sons to grow up, Molly
Cogan decided it was time to return home.
Home to Sweetgrass Montana.
Home to her grandfather's ranch.

*"Debbie Macomber's name on a book is a guarantee
of delightful, warm-hearted romance."*

—Jayne Ann Krentz

1-55166-400-3
AVAILABLE IN PAPERBACK
FROM AUGUST, 1998

RONA JAFFE

Five Women

Once a week, five women meet over dinner and
drinks at the Yellowbird, their favourite
Manhattan bar. To the shared table they bring
their troubled pasts; their hidden secrets.
And through their friendship, each will find
a courageous new beginning.

Five Women is an *"insightful look at female
relationships."*

—Publishers Weekly

1-55166-424-0
**AVAILABLE IN PAPERBACK
FROM AUGUST, 1998**

ORD INK

We are giving away a year's supply of Mills & Boon® books to the five lucky winners of our latest competition. Simply fill in the ten missing words below, complete the coupon overleaf and send this entire page to us by 28th February 1999. The first five correct entries will each win a year's subscription to the Mills & Boon series of their choice. What could be easier?

BUSINESS	**SUIT**	CASE
BOTTLE		HAT
FRONT		BELL
PARTY		BOX
SHOE		PIPE
RAIN		TIE
ARM		MAN
SIDE		ROOM
BEACH		GOWN
FOOT		KIND
BIRTHDAY		BOARD

Please turn over for details of how to enter ➪

C8H

HOW TO ENTER

There are ten words missing from our list overleaf. Each of the missing words must link up with the two on either side to make a new word or words.

For example, 'Business' links with 'Suit' and 'Case' to form 'Business Suit' and 'Suit Case':

BUSINESS—SUIT—CASE

As you find each one, write it in the space provided. When you have linked up all the words, fill in the coupon below, pop this page into an envelope and post it today. Don't forget you could win a year's supply of Mills & Boon® books—you don't even need to pay for a stamp!

Mills & Boon Word Link Competition
FREEPOST CN81, Croydon, Surrey, CR9 3WZ
EIRE readers: (please affix stamp) PO Box 4546, Dublin 24.

Please tick the series you would like to receive if you are one of the lucky winners

Presents™ ❑ Enchanted™ ❑ Medical Romance™ ❑
Historical Romance™ ❑ Temptation®

Are you a Reader Service™ subscriber?   Yes ❑   No ❑

Ms/Mrs/Miss/Mr ....Initials..........................
                                    (BLOCK CAPITALS PLEASE)
Surname..

Address ....

....

....Postcode.........................

(I am over 18 years of age)   C8H

Closing date for entries is 28th February 1999.
One entry per household. Competition open to residents of the
UK and Ireland only. You may be mailed with offers from other
reputable companies as a result of this application. If you would
prefer not to receive such offers, please tick this box. ❑

Mills & Boon is a registered trademark
owned by Harlequin Mills & Boon Limited